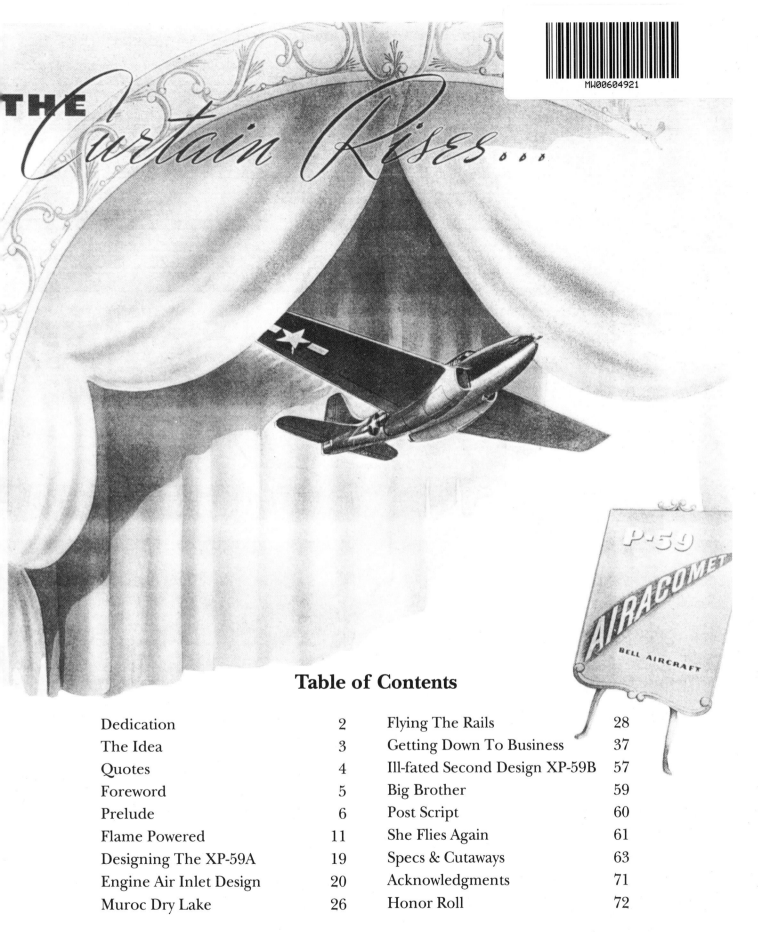

THE Curtain Rises...

Table of Contents

Jet Pioneers of America
a ❤ Book
IBNS 0 - 9633387 - 0 - 6

ON THIS SITE THE FIRST AMERICAN
MADE JET ENGINE WAS BUILT AND
TESTED. THIS ENGINE POWERED
THE FIRST GAS TURBINE AIRCRAFT
FLOWN IN THE UNITED STATES
OF AMERICA – OCTOBER 1942.
JET PIONEERS ASSOCIATION
OF THE UNITED STATES OF AMERICA

This book is dedicated to Jet Pioneers around the world whose early efforts led to the development of an industry that has profoundly changed the world. Their creative energies and visions, carried forth in times of great strife, have left a heritage in which they and their descendants can take great pride.

The Idea

The intense pressure of war, which has always given great impetus to rapid technological progress, produced major improvements in the 1930's and 1940's pertaining to design, engineering and performance of Military aircraft. These and many other steps required pioneers with eyes turned to the future, to now seek ways to overcome the known inefficiencies of the piston engine. This desire, for new forms of propulsion, <u>eventually</u> led to the development of the jet engine. Sadly it could have come much sooner except for "The great obstacle" which turned out to be "<u>The Idea</u>" itself. And so success waited for people, in high places, who would come to accept "The Idea" that hot gases exiting a pipe at some 1400 $^{Ft.}$/sec could, in fact, propel a plane faster and higher than a 1000+ hp piston engine turning a propeller.

The Author

"Truly 50% of the 'Technical People' at attendance for the first flight of the (British) Gloster E 28/39 did not really think it would work ...

"When I asked for an official photographer be sent from the Air Ministry, none was sent - such was the lack of interest in that historic event."

John Johnson, Whittle Aide 1941

"Gentlemen: I give you the Whittle Engine - consult all you wish and arrive at any decision you please - just as long as General Electric accepts a contract to build fifteen of them."

General H.H. Arnold, Secret Meeting with GE 9/4/41 Wash, DC

"That plane! (XP-59A) will fly with no prop ... all I see is a 6 ft flame ... what is it flame powered?" [snicker].

overheard remark at an early 1943 demo flight.

"It's all over for us boys."

Larry Bell (to his Muroc Crew) after seeing the P-80 Shooting Star Circa January 1944

"It's nice to be first – but the money is in being second."

Larry Bell 1940s

Foreword

The aircraft industry today is an incredibly demanding business, of both material technology and individuals. That also held true for the group of pioneers that accepted the challenge in 1941 to design and build the XP-59A and its unique form of gas turbine propulsion. Early progress on this unique challenge was a process of building upon past accomplishments and learning from both experience and from heart-wrenching failure. It is this process that <u>Flame Powered</u> chronicles, giving credit to the extraordinary individuals, the virgin technology and the whirl of world events, that made the development of the XP-59A a worthwhile and challenging event in the midst of World War II.

When one surveys all the pioneer "jet–propelled" aircraft that preceded the XP-59A, it is essential to point out that at the time (Circa 1941 - 1942) the term jet propulsion was different than our present day concept. At that time, the term better compared to what we refer to today as "rocket propulsion" or non-air breathing engines. An example of this concept would be the German Heinkel He 176 powered by a Walter rocket engine of 1100 lbs of thrust or the German ME163 Komet powered by a 1650 lb Walter rocket engine. Of further note, is the fact that the XP-59A Airacomet and its engines were, from inception, to be the first turbine powered <u>production</u> fighter aircraft for use by an Air Force. All earlier "First Flight" pioneers were prototypes or demo-proof of concept machines like the turbine powered Heinkel He 178, the hybrid Italian Caproni - Campini CC - 2 and the British Gloster E.28/39, never of themselves to go into production.

Although the Airacomet officially flew on October 2, 1942, it was not until January 6, 1944, that a vague, pictureless press release was given by the Pentagon. The release of photographs would not come to light until September 1944. The shadow of secrecy that hung over this project acted to prevent those individuals associated with it from receiving the credit that they justly deserved. Unfortunately, by the time the details of the XP-59A and its revolutionary propulsion system could be revealed, the airplane had already taken on the role of a trainer with the Lockheed P-80 Shooting Star receiving all the limelight of press and media attention. It is now, after fifty years, that this book (the first wholly dedicated to this specific project) will attempt to right that injustice.

Actual Stamp for Bell's Special Secret Project
No. MX-397. The XP-59A.

5

Prelude

Gas turbines for primary power . . . still in the lab — 1930s —

If turbosuperchargers had moved out of the laboratory in the '30s, basic gas turbine research and the hint of gas turbine use as a primary source of power certainly had not.

In 1936 Wright Field prepared a report, "The Gas Turbine as a Prime Mover for Aircraft." In 1936 and 1937, GE completed several research bulletins and engineering reports on gas turbines for stationary powerplants. In February, 1937, GE submitted a paper to Wright Field entitled "Gas Turbine Power Plants for Aeronautical Applications" that focused on using the gas turbine to drive a propeller – certainly one of the first studies of the turboprop engine.

In the summer of 1939, a study was prepared at GE in Lynn, Mass. on "Jet Propulsion Gas Turbines" and forwarded to Schenectady to Dale D. Streid – later to become one of GE's best known jet engine technologists – for comment. Although Streid was "pessimistic" at the outset about this use of gas turbines because of the high temperatures required, he was invited to Lynn and soon became convinced of the gas turbine's potential for aircraft. In September, 1939, Streid wrote "optimistically" about jet propulsion for speeds of 450 miles per hour or more in a memo with the prophetic heading, "Airplane Propulsion by Means of a Jet Reaction and Gas Turbine Power Plant." Even earlier in the century Sanford Moss, later to become GE's world famous turbocharger designer, had for his doctoral thesis, began theoretical examination of the gas turbine and, in laboratory experiments conducted in 1903,

Le Pere P 59 (1919) Early use of a GE Turbo Super Charger - Note Model No. of Plane is the same as the Jet.(Photo courtesy of GEAE)

Aviation Pioneers-Frank Whittle, British turbojet inventor, shakes hands with Dr. Moss. Whittle visited GE in 1942 to consult on the development of his jet engine by GE.(Photo courtesy of GEAE)

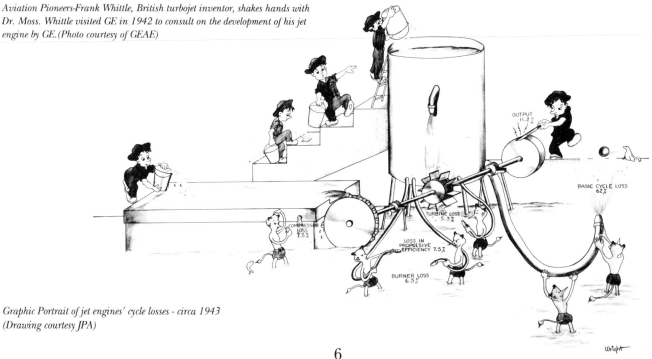

Graphic Portrait of jet engines' cycle losses - circa 1943 (Drawing courtesy JPA)

achieved what no other man had successfully done previously: produce energy to operate a turbine by burning gas in a pressurized chamber. Some thirty years later Dr. Moss while in England reported on the gas turbine work under way at British Thomson-Houston Company (an offspring of the original U.S. GE company), including some of the early "exhaust gas turbines . . . for airplane service." Moss had in fact observed the initial Whittle efforts.

The compilation of data . . . the exchange of ideas... the sharing of technology breakthroughs . . . had begun. The first glimmerings of jet flight had been taking place on both sides of the Atlantic in the decade of the 1930s.

Parallel – but separate – developments

Gas turbine work progressed slowly in the U.S. in the 30's. But Britain and Germany – independently and unknown to each other – were making rapid progress in turbines as a primary source of aircraft propulsion. Despite their separate developments, Britain and Germany shared a common motivation: military requirements.

In Germany, Hans von Ohain, a University of Goettingen aerodynamics student, patented a turbojet engine design in 1935. While similar to Whittle's concept, it was different in many important details. In 1936, von Ohain's professor, who knew Ernst Heinkel, president of the famous Heinkel aircraft company, prevailed upon him to hire the young student to develop the engine. A 550-pound thrust engine was built and demonstrated by March, 1937, convincing the company that work should proceed on a flight engine. Von Ohain began work on a 1,980-pound thrust engine and the aircraft designers laid plans for an airframe to utilize the powerplant.

When the first engine did not meet specifications, a modified version producing 1,100 pounds of thrust was built and substituted in the completed He 178 airframe.

In total secrecy – even from Third Reich officials in Berlin – plans were made for a first flight at dawn on a Sunday morning in August, 1939. The site chosen was a Heinkel airfield at Marienehe near the north coast of Germany, along the Baltic. At that latitude, the sun rose about four a.m. in the summer.

An active Luftwaffe test pilot who was also attached to the Heinkel staff, Erich Warsitz, had been chosen for the flight. Because of Ernst Heinkel's impatience, no preliminary taxi tests were made. When Warsitz was convinced the engine was not going to explode as he made his ground runup he taxied out for the flight with a cloud of dust from the jet exhaust trailing behind him. Within seconds, the He178, powered by von Ohain's He S-3b turbojet engine, lifted from the Marienehe runway. The world's first jet flight was underway—August 27, 1939.

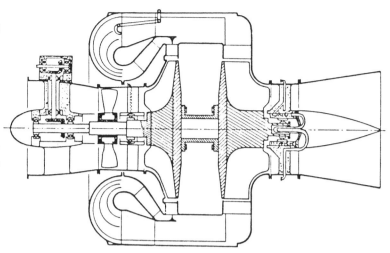

German Heinkel HeS3b (1937) 992lbs of thrust powered the He178 - note centrifugal compressor and centrifugal turbine designed by Hans von Ohain. (Photo courtesy of JPA)

Dr. Hans von Ohain with cutaway model of the HeS3b jet engine. (Photo courtesy of GEAE)

The Little Heinkel He178 - 24'6" in length - only 3565lbs empty wtg. First flight August 27, 1939. (Photo courtesy of GEAE)

Sir Frank Whittle and his W.1 engine. (Photo courtesy of GEAE)

British Gloster E.28/39 "pioneer". First flew May 15, 1941 with the Whittle W.1 engine. (Photo courtesy GEAE)

Japanese Najajima "Kikka". Flew August 7, 1945 in between the dropping of the two atom bombs. (Photo courtesy of GEAE)

Italy with it's Caproni-Campini CC-2. First flew August 17, 1940 . Had a piston powered compressor. (Photo courtesy of GEAE)

Although Warsitz encountered trouble retracting the landing gear, the engine performed without flaw. After a relatively short, low level flight, he landed the He 178, finally bringing it to a stop on the runway—just short of the Warnow River.

Five days later—September 1, 1939—Hitler's armies invaded Poland. The gas turbine development race took on a new urgency.

Meanwhile, in Britain, RAF officer Frank Whittle already had a 1930 British patent for his jet engine.

His decade-long struggle against the bureaucracy and the "snicker/can't-do-that" philosophy had begun in that year. Reporting his patent to the Air Ministry — as required of a military officer — he received discouraging news: the government was not interested. As a result, the invention was not classified under any secrecy order and, in a year and a half, the details soon began appearing in technical journals — including some in Germany and the U.S.

Whittle applied for and was enrolled in advanced engineering studies at Peterhouse College, Cambridge. During this time, his patent came up for renewal. Whittle, with a growing family and the world still in the throes of a depression, couldn't afford the five pounds renewal fee. The patent lapsed.

But help arrived unexpectedly in 1935. An ex-Royal Air Force officer who knew Whittle and remembered his convictions about the jet engine and another former RAF officer offered to support and promote Whittle's efforts. By the fall, the investment house of O.T. Falk & Partners, Ltd. had agreed to finance the project and the firm of Power Jets, Ltd. was formed. Power Jets then let a design contract to British Thomson-Houston, where Dr. Moss and others from GE saw the engine work during their visits to BTH.

Work continued at BTH for nearly four years. The RAF had given tacit approval (but no funds or recognition) to the project by permitting the young flight officer to devote part-time effort to the Power Jets firm.

Whittle and his team of pioneers had recurring problems in the combustion and turbine sections, including turbine failures and even engine explosions. BTH employees, in fear because of the sounds, smells and vibrations caused by the engine testing, complained to their management. Whittle and his "folly" were dispatched to an empty BTH factory near Coventry.

Finally, in July, 1939, the Air Ministry awarded Power Jets a contract for an experimental jet engine to power a specially designed airplane which Gloster Aircraft Company would build. The engine, designated W.1, was to develop 855 pounds of thrust. The aircraft was designated the E.28/39. The engine/airframe combination would set the stage for the Allies' first jet flight in the next decade.

Today, the Gloster E.28/39, Serial No. W 4041/G, is preserved by the aeronautical collection of the Science Museum, South Kensington, London, England. The "G" at the end of the serial number indicated that an armed guard was required for the airplane.

The end of an eventful decade

As the '30s came to a close, the gas turbine seeds that had been sown in the late 1800s were finally beginning to bud. . . some more vigorously than others. . . but all were coming to life.

In Germany, a jet aircraft had already flown. In Britain, hardware for an engine had been built and tested; an airplane was in the design stages. In the U.S., gas turbine work had been concentrated on turbosupershargers, but a handful of Army Air Corps and GE visionaries had taken the first steps toward the realization of a true jet powerplant.

Even Japan began some gas turbine work in 1937 when the Japanese Navy purchased Swiss Brown-Boveri engines with an eye toward adapting them for aviation use. Italy also started gas turbine studies in 1933 when engineer Secondo Campini proposed the use of an airplane fuselage as a giant cylinder for aircraft jet propulsion. And so most of the key protagonists of a soon-to-be declared World War were reacting to military requirements with increased action.

1941 is a pivotal year

In January, 1941 the National Academy of Sciences, fully aware of the many gas turbine studies underway in the U.S. and Europe, urged that turbines be developed to power ships. The NAS report was an impetus to gas turbine development, but the study also concluded that gas turbines would be impractical for aircraft propulsion because they would weigh 13 pounds for every unit of horsepower delivered—in contrast to the then current piston engines approaching the production of one horsepower for every pound of weight.

As a result of the NAS report, the three leading U.S. manufacturers of turbines—GE, Allis Chalmers and Westinghouse—had been awarded U.S. Navy contracts to study marine gas turbines. It was under this contract that the GE Schenectady Steam Turbine division work on a PT boat powerplant was being undertaken.

During the same period U.S. intelligence sources had received scattered information on the German Jet engine effort (they did not know the He 178 had already flown, although a British agent had seen the first flight) and, of course, were well aware of the British hardware work.

On February 25, 1941, General H.H. Arnold, Deputy Chief of Staff for Air (who later commanded all U.S. Army Air Forces in World War II and is called "the Father of the United States Air Force"), wrote to Dr. Vannevar Bush, chairman of NACA (and later renowned for his work on the atomic bomb), urging NACA to form a jet research group. At the time, rocket propulsion was linked with jet propulsion and the implication was that the study group was to include that form of aircraft propulsion in its charter.

In March, Dr. Bush created a "Special Committee on Jet Propulsion" within NACA. The committee was headed by Dr. Will Durand, Dr. Moss' Cornell professor and the chairman of NACA during World War I. Dr. Durand, of course, had promoted the development of the turbosupercharger during the 1914-1918 conflict. The committee included representatives from the Army Air Corps, Navy Bureau of Aeronautics, National Bureau of Standards, Johns Hopkins University and Massachusetts Institute of Technology, and from the three U.S. turbine manufacturers – Allis Chalmers, Westinghouse and General Electric. The inclusion of representatives from the companies was significant both in the intended direction of the work of the committee and in the ultimate outcome of aircraft gas turbine work in the U.S.

General Arnold had specifically requested that the then-leading U.S. manufacturers of aircraft engines not be included on the committee. His reason was apparently that they were heavily involved in the wartime military aircraft buildup plus the fact that aircraft gas turbines were unorthodox and entirely different from the piston engines used to power airplanes since the original flight of the Wright brothers in 1903.

In June the three gas turbine manufacturers submitted engine proposals – all based on axial flow compressors. Allis Chalmers' proposal was for a ducted-fan engine (in effect, an encased multi-bladed propeller which served as an added compressor providing extra air); Westinghouse selected a pure turbojet; and GE, basing its proposal on the Schenectady studies, submitted a turboprop.

By July, 1941, NACA had decided to give the three manufacturers an OK to proceed with development work. On July 7, 1941, GE started design in Schenectady of the world's first turboprop engine. In September, the Durand committee recommended that all three projects be carried forward by the U.S. military services. By the following month the Army and Navy had assumed leadership of aircraft engine development and by early 1942 Allis Chalmers and Westinghouse were under contract to the Navy, GE to the Army Air Corps.

An intriguing sidelight to these events of late 1941 - early 1942 was that each service had contracted for engines it didn't really want. The Navy was more interested in the GE turboprop, but the Air Corps contracted for it; the Army was more interested in the turbojet and ducted fan, but the Navy became the contracting authority.

The Bell P-59A Airacomet The United States' First Jet Aircraft

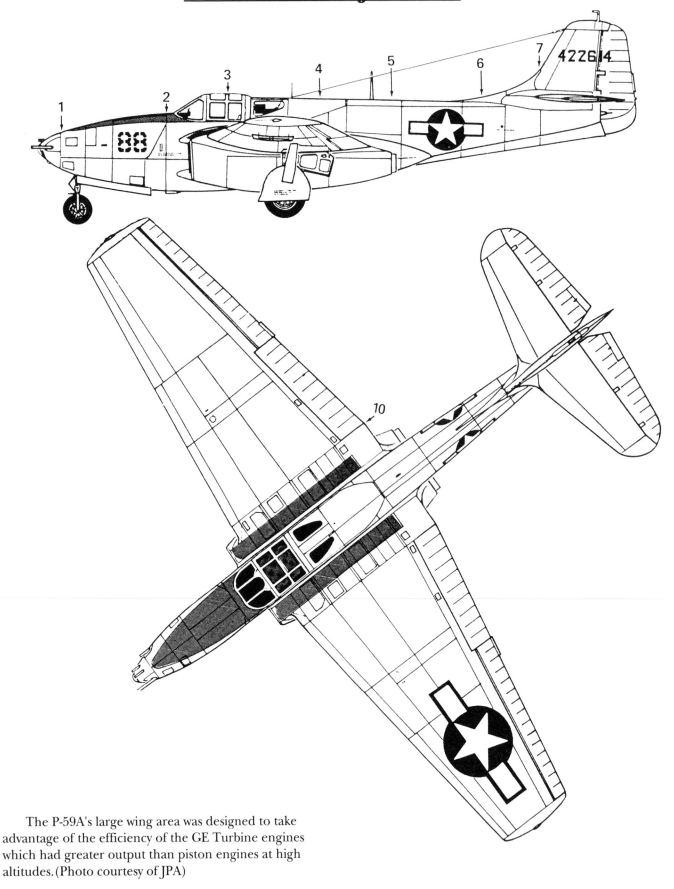

The P-59A's large wing area was designed to take advantage of the efficiency of the GE Turbine engines which had greater output than piston engines at high altitudes.(Photo courtesy of JPA)

Flame Powered – The Temperature Is Rising

In April 1941, while in England, General Arnold, who was chief of the Army Air Force, finally had the opportunity to review, first-hand, the English developments in the jet propulsion field when he had the occasion to examine the Whittle gas turbine engine and Gloster E.28/39 airplane. During this visit, he also had the opportunity to witness both taxiing and short flight tests of the airplane. Realizing the full importance of these developments, he discussed the gas turbine question further with Lord Beaverbrook, Sir Henry Tizard, Colonel Moore-Brabazon and Sir Charles Portal. As a result of these discussions, preliminary arrangements were made for providing information on the Whittle engine to General Arnold's London technical staff for their evaluation.

General Arnold returned to the United States in May. He at once informed Brig. General Frank Carroll, Chief of the Engineering Division at Wright Field, and Brig. General Oliver P. Echols, A-4, on the Air Staff at the Army Air Force Headquarters in Washington, of the forthcoming development and production efforts that would probably be required in the field of gas turbine engines. He also advised the State Department of his findings and requested their assistance in making the necessary arrangements for establishing the desired liaison between the two countries to facilitate the exchange of information in the gas turbine area. In order to insure the necessary cooperation between the United States and England, a series of negotiations were then undertaken between Cordell Hull, United States Secretary of State, and the Earl of Halifax, then British Ambassador to the United States.

As a result of these combined efforts, a very important meeting took place on July 22, 1941, at the Ministry of Aircraft Production in London. At this meeting, Air Marshall Linnell of the MAP and Dr. Roxbee Cox of Power Jets Ltd. briefed Colonel A. J. Lyon and Mr. D. R. Shoults of General Electric, on gas turbine developments in the United Kingdom. On July 25, Colonel Lyon, Mr. Shoults, and Major Carl Brandt visited the Power Jets, Ltd. facilities and discussed gas turbine progress with Wing Commander Whittle. Three days later, this same group visited the Gloster Aircraft Company's factory and viewed the two E.28/39 experimental aircraft then under development. During this visit, details of the F.9/40, twin engine fighter design (later versions of which would be known as the Meteor) were also discussed.

Colonel Lyon was General Arnold's Representative in England for all technical matters. Mr. Shoults was a Technical Service Representative for the General Electric Company and he had originally been sent to England by General Electric to advise and assist Colonel

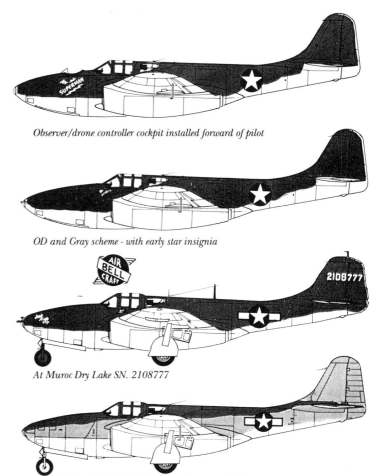

Observer/drone controller cockpit installed forward of pilot

OD and Gray scheme - with early star insignia

At Muroc Dry Lake SN. 2108777

Navy (BuNo 63960) NAS Pax River January - 1944
(All of the above courtesy of Aerophile)

Lyon in the servicing and use of General Electric turbo-supercharger equipment being used in the Lend-Lease B-17C airplanes. However, with the new and growing emphasis on gas turbine engines, General Arnold had appointed Mr. Shoults to act jointly with Colonel Lyon as an Investigating Committee on the new engine. In order to evaluate the technical aspects of the English jet-powered airplanes, Colonel Lyon had requested Major Brandt to serve on the Committee and to report on this phase of the program.

In late July, Major Donald J. Keirn arrived in England on a secret mission and upon reporting to Colonel Lyon, he found that the had been appointed by General Arnold to be Colonel Lyon's Deputy on the jet propulsion project. After being brought up to date on the British developments in the gas turbine field, Major Keirn was sent to Lutterworth where the Power Jets factory was located. There, he could gain first hand information on this effort and evaluate it with respect to possible American utilization. Arriving at Lutterworth, he met Frank Whittle for the first time and for the next four days he went over the details of the Whittle engine. Returning to London, he again reported to Colonel Lyon and made the recommendation that the United States build a copy of the Whittle design.

11

Historic Meeting

In order to present the results of their findings regarding possible United States participation in the gas turbine field, Mr. Shoults and Major Brandt returned to the United States, and at the now historic September 4th meeting in Washington D.C., they presented the recommendations of the London Committee. The Government and the Army Air Force were represented at this meeting by Mr. Robert A. Lovett, Assistant Secretary of War for Air; Major General H. H. Arnold, Chief AAF; Brig. General Carl A. Spaatz, Chief of the Air Staff; Brig. General Oliver P. Echols, Chief of the Material Division; Lt. Colonel Benjamin W. Chidlaw, Material Division; and Major Brandt. The General Electric Company was represented by Dr. A. R. Stevenson, Jr., Mr. R. C. Muir, Mr. S. R. Puffer, and Mr. Shoults. At this meeting, after hearing and discussing the recommendations, it was tentatively decided that 15 engines and three airplanes should be produced as soon as possible. Due to the low thrust output of the Whittle engine, it was decided that the airplane should be of a twin engine design with Bell Aircraft Corporation being selected as the first choice to build the airplane.

A small safe sat in the corner of the office where this high powered group of military and industrial officials met. General Arnold turned the combination to the proper settings, opened the safe and took out a sheaf of drawings and reports. After a presentation on the details of the British project by Roy Shoults and Major Brandt, General Arnold said, "Gentlemen, I give you the Whittle engine. Consult all you wish and arrive at any decision you please - just so long as General Electric accepts a contract to build 15 of them."

The official reason given for selecting Bell as the airframe manufacturer was listed as being its close proximity to the General Electric facilities. However, as with most major decisions, any final conclusion or recommendation is usually not the result of one factor.

Rather, it represents the best judgment based upon several considerations and such was the case in the selection of Bell. In a letter to R. Neal in 1966, General B. W. Chidlaw, USAF (Ret.)., elaborated on this point and made the following remarks.

"Quite naturally, all aircraft companies experienced in Fighter Aircraft Design and Production, entered into our early considerations. My recommendation as to the choice of Bell (on the airframe side) hinged mostly around the following considerations:

"1) Most all of the other companies previously experienced in Fighter Design and Production found their Design and Engineering Staffs so overloaded with work improving and/or 'debugging' the aircraft already under development or production, that I did not wish to see them further overloaded with undertaking still another project of this magnitude - particularly within the completion time span of one year which General Arnold had decreed for the first phase completion of this highly experimental project.

"2) Bell had a smaller but highly-experienced and imaginative Engineering Staff, well experienced in Fighter Design. This particular group, at just that time, were less overloaded with current development and production improvement work,

---

WAR DEPARTMENT
OFFICE OF THE CHIEF OF STAFF
WASHINGTON

August 27, 1941

Mr. D. R. Shoults,
c/o General Electric Company,
Schenectady, New York.

Dear Mr. Shoults:

Confirming our conversation of this morning, you are authorized to discuss the Whittle matter with Mr. Muir, Mr. Stevenson, Mr. Puffer, and Mr. Warren.

You will inform these four gentlemen of the secret status of the discussions.

Sincerely,

H. ARNOLD,
Major General, U. S. A.,
Deputy Chief of Staff for Air.

and hence, able to undertake a project of this sort with less interference to other important projects and production programs then on the books.

"3) Bell had certain isolated facilities which could be made readily available to start this project under the strict conditions of the "SECRET" classification as imposed by General Arnold.

"4) The proximity of Buffalo to the Schenectady and Lynn, (MA.) engine plants of G.E. promised easier, faster and more complete and constant coordination so necessary to both the airframe and engine manufacturers in this project which was, so highly experimental in nature. It must be remembered that in building the Americanized version of the British engine, all measurements had to be translated to American standards and such measurements had to be passed on immediately to the Design Staff of the airframe manufacturer so that both parts of the project could go on concurrently.

"5) Last, but by no means least, we were all aware of Larry Bell's tremendous personal drive and boundless enthusiasm in all matters relating to Research and Development...and we likewise knew that once in this program, Mr. Bell would personally be riding herd...and keeping on top of the project...every minute."

Bell's willingness and capacity to undertake the somewhat unorthodox approach had already been demonstrated by the Bell-designed XFM-1 Airacuda and the XP-39 Airacobra. In the years to come, the ability of the Bell Aircraft Corporation to push forward into new frontiers, would be exemplified by the Bell X-1, X-2, and X-5 research airplanes.

General Electric, of course, had been selected by the Army Air Force as the engine Contractor because of their extensive research and development capabilities in the closely-related field of turbosuperchargers. It is interesting to note that when the NACA Special Committee on Jet Propulsion was first formed, the only industrial companies invited to participate were Westinghouse, Allis-Chalmers, and the Schenectady Steam Turbine Division of General Electric. Representatives from the established aircraft engine companies, i.e., Allison, Pratt & Whitney, etc., were specifically left out of this group at the request of General Arnold. At this time, he feared that the old line firms might possibly be opposed to the development of such an unorthodox form of propulsion.

At the conclusion of the historic September 4 meeting, Arnold had the British Government notified, through the American Embassy in London, that a decision had been reached to produce jet-propelled airplanes and gas turbine engines in the United States. It was also requested that Great Britain send authorization rights covering the reproduction of the Whittle engine, one complete engine and one single airplane (E.28/39) to the United States.

That evening General Arnold's office contacted Larry Bell at his home and requested that he and his Chief Engineer, Mr. Harland M. Poyer, be present for a meeting in Washington the next day. Mr. Bell then quickly contacted Poyer at his home to advise him of the meeting, and late that evening, they both left Buffalo by train for Washington.

Thus, On September 5, in a preliminary meeting with General Echols, Mr. Bell and Mr. Poyer were given a briefing on the reasons for their visit and a resume of progress in the gas turbine field. The records indicate that at this meeting, General Echols asked Mr. Bell to participate in the development of America's first jet-powered airplane and that Mr. Bell, in turn, expressed the willingness of his company to undertake this effort. Since the decision to have Bell build the airplane had already been made the day before, it then seems likely to assume that the act of asking Mr. Bell to participate, was more a matter of form, than an actual request. In any event, the fact that Bell would build the airplane was probably a foregone conclusion! Later that same day, a second meeting took place, this time, in General Arnold's office, with Mr. Bell, Mr. Poyer and Mr. Shoults present, and at this meeting, a final decision was reached to build fifteen gas turbine engines and three airplanes.

After returning to Buffalo, Mr. Poyer selected a small group of his key Engineers and these men (known as the Secret Six) were then called into Mr. Bell's office. They were first sworn to strict secrecy and then given a briefing on the recent Washington trip. Mr. Bell than assigned them the task of designing the XP-59A. This original group consisted of an Aerodynamics Engineer, a Thermodynamics Engineer, a Structural Designer, a Development Engineer, a Stress Analysis Engineer, and a Weights Engineer.

Robert J. Woods and Ray P. Whitman, co-founders, who along with Larry Bell had organized Bell Aircraft corporation on July 10, 1935. Just prior to that time Larry Bell had been Vice-President and General Manger of the Consolidated Aircraft Corporation but when Consolidated moved to California, he resigned his

Back Row: Herb Bowers, R. Shoults, H. Poyers, R. Wolf, E. Rhodes.
Front: Col. R. Swofford, Capt. Schulte, Major D. Keirn. Key project members at Larry Bells office, Dec. 15, 1941. (Photo courtesy of R. Wolf)

(Photo courtesy of R. Wolf)

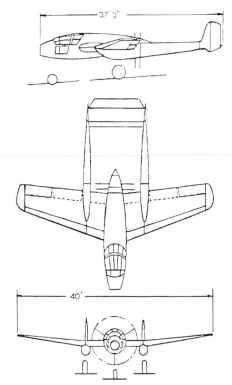

XP-59 wooden mock up never produced but used to make it appear that the jet project was a modification to this model. (Drawing courtesy of AAHS)

position and remained in Buffalo to form his own company,. Initially, 40,000 square feet of space in Consolidated's old building was rented and by the end of 1935, Bell Aircraft Corporation employed all of 60 people. The first airplane design to be produced by Bell was the XFM-1 Airacuda which first flew on September 1, 1937,.

With only one small free-hand sketch of the engine and working under extreme security measures, this group of six men, within the short span of two weeks, prepared a proposal and a 1/20 scale model of the airplane. The proposal was presented to and approved by General Arnold. On September 30, 1941, a fixed fee Contract W535 AC-21931 was entered into with the Bell Aircraft Corporation for three XP-59A airplanes, and data for a total price of $1,644,431. The XP-59A airplanes, were described in the Contract only as "twin engine, single place interceptor pursuit models". General Echols had recommended the approval of this Contract with the comment that this airplane was needed in connection with the development of high performance interceptor pursuit airplanes. The Contract was approved by the Under Secretary of War on October 3, 1941 and it called for the first airplane to be delivered eight months from the date of the Contract approval, a rather tight schedule, considering the magnitude of the project. The guidelines given for the design of the airplane were very loose, with Bell being given a free hand in determining the configuration of the airplane. The only basic requirement was that they wrap an airframe around the two forthcoming General Electric engines.

Throughout the entire XP-59A effort, tight security measures were constantly imposed on the project and from the beginning, it was given a special secret classification. In fact, the designation for the airplane, XP-59A, was not original but rather was borrowed from a Bell experimental model that had been assigned the designation XP-59. The XP-59 was to be a 450 mile per hour single engine interceptor with twin tail blooms, dual rotating pusher propellers and a tricycle landing gear. The armament for the final version was to be four .50 caliber machine guns and two 20 mm cannons and the airplane was to be powered by a two-stage Pratt & Whitney R-2800-23 engine. The original Army Air Force Contract called for the procurement of two airplanes of this type but the program never progressed further than a partial mock-up and several wind tunnel models and on December 1,1941 the Army Air Force informed Bell that the propeller-driven XP-59 project would be terminated.

When Bell first agreed to participate in the secret jet propulsion program, the question of the airplane designation had arisen. It was then decided to assign the new jet airplane the designation XP-59A so that at least on paper, it would appear to be a modification of the Bell propeller-driven design. Bell Aircraft was to assign Model Number 27 to the XP-59 project.

Colonel Chidlaw was selected by General Arnold and General Echols to head up, monitor and direct the development and testing phases of the XP-59A project. This responsibility also involved the coordination of the activities at Bell and General Electric with the British and Washington. Colonel Chidlaw brought to the project almost twenty years of aviation experience, having joined the Air Service in 1922 as a 2nd Lieutenant immediately after his graduation from the United States Military Academy. Ray Whitman, acting as the Bell Representative, handled the liaison work between Bell, Wright Field and Washington. Major Ralph R. Swofford, Jr. and Major Keirn were assigned as Aircraft Project Officer and Jet Engine Project Officer, respectively. Both of these men reported directly to Colonel Frank O. Carroll, who was Chief of the Experimental Engineering Section at Wright Field.

Just as Bell was beginning to prepare its proposal for the XP-59A airplane, negotiations between the United States and England, concerning details of the Whittle engine, were rapidly reaching completion. In reply to General Arnold's request of September 4, the Military Attache in London advised that drawings and data on the jet engine and one complete engine would be sent to the United States as soon as possible. A single engine airplane was not available and a definite date could not be established for shipping one.

On September 22, 1941, the British Air Commission advised the United State Secretary of War that authority for release of all available information on jet propulsion to the United States had been given by the British Government, However, certain restrictions on the use of the material would first have to be agreed upon by the United States. These restrictions were, (1) the information would be used only for the purpose intended, (2) secrecy would be maintained and commercial rights would be protected, (3) no information would be released to a third party without the concurrence of the British Government, and (4) none but citizens of the United States and subjects of Great Britain (of known background in either case) would be permitted to have knowledge of this information without British consent. On October 9, 1941, these restrictions were officially confirmed by Henry L. Stimson, United States Secretary of War, with only one minor addition, dealing with United States rights of development on independent gas turbine projects.

Whittle W.1 used for taxi test in Gloster E28/39. Later sent to GE Lynn and tested in Bldg 34N November 1941. To help GE team prepare for the I-A testing.(Photo courtesy of GEAE)

All of the jet propulsion projects were originally placed in a "Special Secret" category, and this classification remained in effect until May 1943 when the project was reduced to "Secret". In November 1943, the security classification was reduced to "Confidential" with the actual airplane performance remaining "Secret", and finally, in August 1944 this classification was further reduced to "Restricted". Initially, the XP-59A project was so secret that the Army Air Force Plant Resident at Bell was not even informed of the project's existence until May 1943.

With the initial authorization of September 22, arrangements had been started for the shipment of the requested items to the U.S. Thus, on October 1, 1941, a B-24 Liberator lifted from the runway at Prestwick, Scotland and winged westward across the Atlantic. It is interesting to note that exactly one year later, to the day, the jet-powered XP-59A would make its maiden flight. The destination of the B-24's cargo was the Turbo-Supercharger Department of General Electric's Lynn, MA. plant. The shipment consisted of the W.1X engine, which was concealed under floor boards in the bomb bay, and a set of manufacturing drawings of the Power Jets W.2B engine design. The W.1X engine that was being sent to the United States was the same engine that was used for the initial taxi tests of the E.28/39 and during the nine months while it was being tested by Power Jets, it had accumulated approximately 132 hours of test running. All of this material was accompanied by a three-man Power Jets team and Major Keirn. The airplane arrived at Bolling Field, Washington, D.C. on October 2, after a running battle with a rather uncooperative United States' Customs Department, the still secret and uninspected cargo was finally delivered to the General Electric Plant by Major Keirn.

"Fort Knox" test cell built to test the W.1X and early GE models of the Whittle engine. Ted Rogers looking over on early test. (Photo courtesy of JPA)

To test the Whittle engine, General Electric built a special engine test cell and for security reasons, this cell was built within an existing building with the engine exhaust being ducted into an unused 64 foot chimney. This small engine test cell was constructed of reinforced concrete with the entrance to the test area being through a heavy steel door. The only means for viewing the engine was through a small observation slit. The heavy construction of the cell and extreme precautions taken while running the engine were considered necessary in order to prevent any accidents from occurring that might jeopardize the security of the project. The first test experience in the test cell with the Whittle engine took place in November 1941. The initial engine run-ups were restricted to 10,000 rpm and only after gaining considerable test time and experience on the engine was the speed stepped up to the 14,000 rpm level. The maximum speed of this engine was approximately 17,550 rpm.

Using the W.2B drawings, the General Electric personnel, under the direction of Mr. Donald F. Warner, began to produce a reproduction of this engine. However, detailed inspection of the drawings revealed several omissions and some shortcomings in the overall design of the engine, and General Electric requested that they be permitted to make the missing parts and to incorporate other design details that they felt were necessary. The Army Air Force approved the request with the provision that General Electric should not make any modifications that would adversely affect engine performance. In spite of the many problems that

1957 - 10th year celebration/dedication of site of First Jet to run in America - Lynn, MA March 18 and April 18, 1942. The site is preserved today and the cell is still used to do component testing. (Photo courtesy of JPA)

had to be overcome, the General Electric engine, now known as the Type I-A, made its first run, somewhat unsuccessfully, in the test cell on March 18, 1942, less than six months after the arrival of the drawings! It would take 30 more days and some modifications before a successful run up. Eventually, a total of thirty I-A engines would be produced for the XP-59A program.

The Type I-A was a centrifugal, reverse flow, turbo jet engine that delivered approximately 1,250 pounds of thrust. Just as in the case of the airframe designation, the "I-Series" designation for the jet engine was selected for security reasons. General Electric was then producing aircraft superchargers with the designation "A" through "F" and, therefore, the use of "I", plus the fact that the jet engine was referred to as a turbosupercharger, served to hide the true nature of the project.

Wing Commander Frank Whittle arrived in the United States in early June 1942, the purpose of his visit being to deliver the latest drawings of the new Power Jets W.2/500 engine and to confer with the General Electric people on the development of their I-A engine. From its earliest runs, the I-A engine had suffered from excessive exhaust gas temperatures, and Whittle was instrumental in helping to solve this problem. Commander Whittle returned to England in the first week of August 1942 after having remained here until the problems with the engine were ironed out and units were ready for installation in the number one XP-59A.

Commemorative stone plaque on Test Cell site - Ann Baumgartner - Carl first woman to fly a jet plane with Jet Pioneer President Jerry Henderson during visit in 1977 to the Lynn plant. (Photo courtesy of JPA)

A. Air Inlets	G. Fuel Nozzle
B. Impeller	H. Spark Plug
C. Diffuser	J. Nozzle
D. Combustor Inlet	K. Turbine Wheel
E. Outer Case	L. Shaft
F. Combustor	M. Exhaust Duct

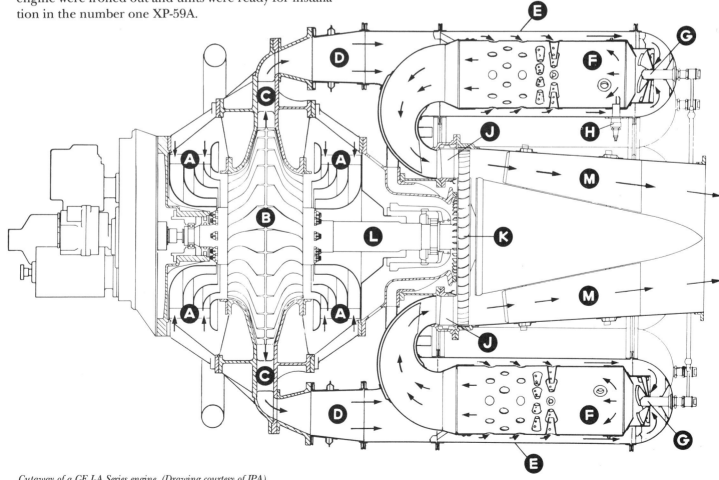

Cutaway of a GE I-A Series engine. (Drawing courtesy of JPA)

Basic Aircraft Design

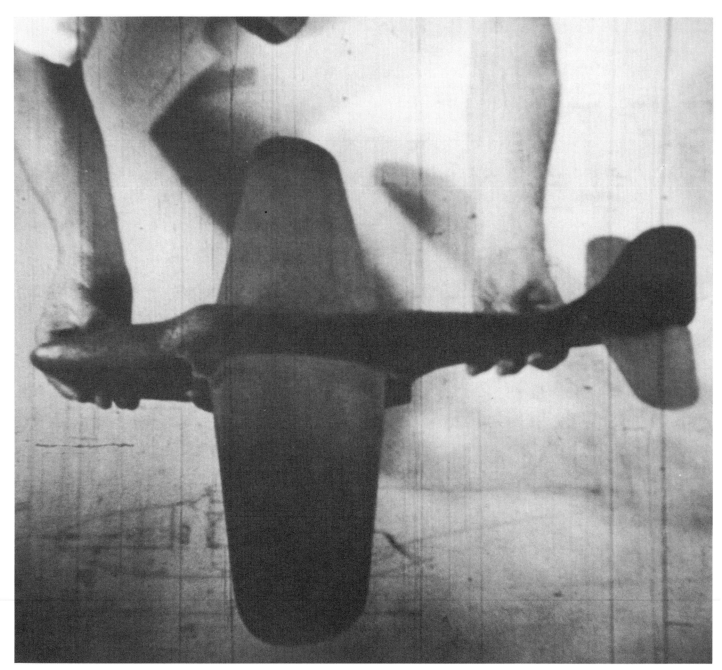

Display model - late 1941 - for preliminary design studies at Bell. Below, XP59A with squared wing tips and reduced span as it emerged from early flight testing at Muroc. (Photo courtesy of JPA)

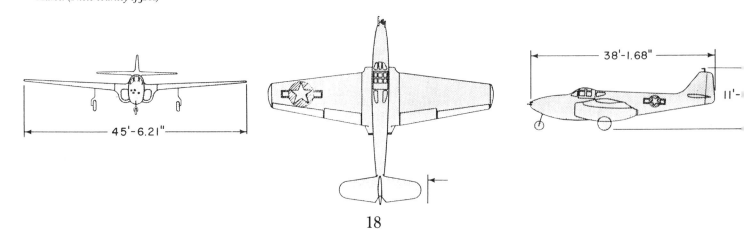

Bell's Buffalo New York site, a former car plant. First XP-59A fuselage built on the second floor, wings built on the second floor also. (Photo courtesy of JPA)

After preparing their proposal and receiving approval of the design, the Bell team had set up the initial XP-59A project in the old Pierce-Arrow Plant which was located on Elmwood Avenue in Buffalo. The original preliminary drawings were made at this location. Before the detail layout stage was reached, however, the project was moved into the second floor of a four story building located at Main and Rodney Streets in Buffalo. At the outset of the program, Bell had realized that a separate area for the Engineering and Shop work would be necessary for the XP-59A effort and so, after some scouting, the "Main Street" Plant was located and leased from the Ford Motor Company. When the project first began moving into the building, the lower floor was still occupied by a Ford Agency. This activity was immediately eased out with Bell then setting up their Machine Shop facilities and storage area on the newly-vacated first floor. All entrances to the building were guarded around the clock and special identification passes were required for entrance to the building. To further insure security, the metal window frames were welded shut and the lower window panes (even on the second floor) were painted over.

Designing the XP-59A

Theoretical analysis of the gas turbine cycle, as a thrust engine and propulsion system, indicated that there should be several advantages over piston engine/propeller driven aircraft. All other things being equal, the turbojet system should produce higher speeds and higher altitudes. These promising trends, which were not yet backed up by either bench testing of real engines or flight experience, led Bell to select aerodynamic features which would optimize performance at 'high' altitudes; i.e.. from 25,000 feet to about 50,000 feet. — a new zone of fighter and interceptor operation.

In terms of overall airplane configuration this meant:

- Larger than usual wings - 25lbs/sq.ft. wing loading

- A pressurized cabin for the pilot

- Materials throughout the airplane that would function properly at extremely low temperatures found at high altitudes.

Along with the many technical uncertainties, Bell faced some seriously inhibiting policies which cast their shadows on the future of the XP-59A even as we were designing it. A few examples:

- General Arnold had very high hopes that two Whittle type W.X engines could produce a militarily – superior fighter with speeds approaching 500 miles per hour. This meant carrying a full military load, including such items as bullet-proof fuel tanks, armor plate to protect the pilot, a bullet-proof windshield and many other weight-adding features which increase wing area and reduce top speed. We were very skeptical of his great expectations from these tiny engines, but proceeded to "overload" the "demonstrator."

- Secrecy and pressures of time prevented Bell from using the nations' high speed wind tunnels to refine design and improve performance — customary "tools" used to reduce drag to a minimum, fine-tune stability and control optimize air inlets etc. One exception was use of the Wright Field low speed wind tunnel to refine the engine air inlets by use of boundary layer control.

- A constant concern was the haunting uncertainty of how much thrust that first engine of GE's own redesign, the I-A, would actually develop. Also, how would its thrust vary with altitude and speed? From the very beginning Bell had frequent qualms about the plane even when the I-A would reach its anticipated design thrust. The ratio of available thrust to total aircraft weight — T/W — would still be too low, compared to current fighters within their lower altitude operating region. Much more thrust and better fuel efficiency would be needed to achieve all-around military superiority. Disheartening as that goal sometimes seemed during the design phase, these shadows were inevitably dispelled by the sheer excitement of being a part of a great technological break-through and becoming true jet pioneers. The designers at Bell knew in their bones that, if they succeeded in igniting the spark, great progress was sure to follow.

Thus, because of the above constraints, the Secret Six had many hours of anxious discussion, making rough weight estimates, crude small scale layouts of possible aircraft configurations, calculating rough performance characteristics and finally coming to the conclusion to <u>go for high altitude</u> and put the engines side-by-side at the center of symmetry.

Once "fixed" there would be no mid-course changes in basic airplane configuration, based on wind tunnel tests and engine development. Whether or not our decisions and estimates were correct, would be proven only by actual flight testing a year or more later.

Bob Wolf responsible for the general Airframe Structure and the Propulsion System Installation probably had more anxiety about engine development than did his design-mates.

For example:

It was customary, when starting a new airplane design, to have large (1/4 or 1/2) scale detailed drawings of the engine to be used. Sometimes an actual engine would even be provided by the manufacturer for purposed engineering reference. Thus, one could proceed with the propulsion system design (engine, propeller, fuel system, cooling system, controls and accessories, etc.) with assurance that the total system would fit into the airframe and function properly.

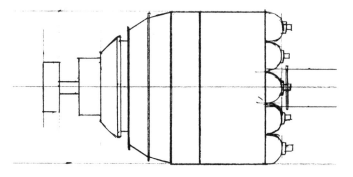

Actual engine sketch used to design engine bays in XP-59A - Bell had little to go by during the early design phase. (Photo courtesy of R. Wolf)

In this case, with such information lacking, one can understand why they were constantly "champing at the bit" and "chewing their nails." What did this engine look like? What were its dimensions, its weight, its thrust, its attachment points, its accessories, cooling requirements, air inflow and jet outflow requirements, jet cone angle, etc., etc.???

Also during the early few weeks they had only a tiny 1/20th scale outline sketch of the engine, about the size of a package of Camel cigarettes, to guide them during that critical time of setting the basic configuration of the

airplane. It was like looking through the wrong end of a pair of field glasses. Bob Wolf noted, ". . . we 'blew up' this miniature sketch to make it more manageable but most of our needs were still unmet."

Regarding thrust characteristics, fuel consumption and weight, they were practically at a standstill in making a realistic estimate of airplane weight and performance.

Engine Air Inlet Design

The XP-59A's engines were located as near as possible to the center of the airplane almost touching each other. The purpose of this arrangement was to reduce drag, and avoid possible difficulties of single-engine flight in case of an engine failure. This close-coupling raised a new concern regarding air inlet design; the threat of boundary layer turbulence which could hamper ram pressure recovery at the inlet. High efficiency of ram air pressure recovery at the engine air intake is very important in reaching maximum thrust at high flight speeds. Therefore, boundary layer turbulence generated along the fuselage sides can be a hindrance to 'clean' airflow into the nacelle inlet. The problem was circumvented by building-in a boundary layer removal system.

In order to determine the best possible geometry of this system, a wind tunnel would be necessary because a suitable low pressure spot not too far from the nacelle inlet must be found as an exit point to draw off the boundary layer flow. This concern was pointed out to Col. Keirn, who made arrangements for us to use the Wright Field low speed wind tunnel to refine the details; a 25-30% improvement in ram pressure recovery was indicated. This was the only 'deviation' from the policy of "No Wind tunnels" set by Genernal Arnold.

In June 1942, Colonel Chidlaw reported that the XP-59A project was being handicapped by the requirement of secrecy which permitted tunnel testing in the Wright Field facility only. He went on to comment that the engine performance for the General Electric engine was in poor agreement with the original calculations, partly because the original engine calculations were based on small scale model data that had to be extrapolated from the Wright Field tunnel test. Another factor that did not help was that the British W.2B engine, which was the basis for the "I" series, was designed for a static sea level thrust of 1,760 pounds of thrust being the maximum obtainable. In line with this fact, Colonel Keirn and Mr. Shoults, in an Institute of the Aeronautical Sciences paper, presented in August 1945 stated:

"Performance predictions for this aircraft (XP-59A) were based on estimated design performance characteristics furnished from England in lieu of

United States engine test data. Unfortunately, neither the original nor the later production engines produced the output predicted."

One of the many problems that confronted the Bell design team was that the secrecy of the project prevented any contact with outside technical experts (NACA) or any of the aircraft equipment vendors. They were then forced to either design and build all of the parts and equipment for the airplane or purchase readily available "off the shelf" components. Many of the major pieces of the airplanes were fabricated in the first floor Machine Shop but large or specialized parts had to be farmed out to the main Bell Plant facilities. To disguise their true nature, the drawings that had to be sent to the main plant for fabrication were deliberately mistitled. An example of this practice was the engine exhaust pipe that was labeled as a "heater duct". No doubt the sheet metal man who received a drawing calling for a 14-inch heater duct was convinced that he was working on a part for one of the world's largest airplanes. The actual assembly of the three XP-59A airplanes was carried out on the second floor of the building. Manufacture of the number one airplane began on January 9, 1942 with the assembly work on the wing and fuselage occurring during March and April.

As finally formalized, the design of the jet-powered XP-59A bore a strong family resemblance to the piston-engine Bell designs, the P-39 and P-63. This was a natural occurrence, since the extremely short time allowed for development of the airplane almost precluded any major advances in the state of the art. Also, the secrecy of the project dictated that Bell draw on its own design team, without additional hiring, and these people in turn, used their design experience with the piston-powered airplane. Furthermore, the purpose of the project was to design, build, and fly a jet-propelled airplane as quickly as possible in order to provide the United States with experience with this new type of power plant. The XP-59A was also unique in that from the beginning of the project, it was proposed to build an airplane that would result in a production fighter. Commenting on the purpose of the XP-59A project, General Chidlaw remarked:

"...we wished to start this project primarily in a Fighter Configuration as a 'Fighter prototype' test bed hoping that we could later expedite (with the development of greater thrust from the Americanized version of the Whittle engine and the addition of adequate armament) the translation from the initial experimental test airplane(s) To a usable 'superior performance' fighter, capable of being produced in quantity for our then Army Air Force fighter units".

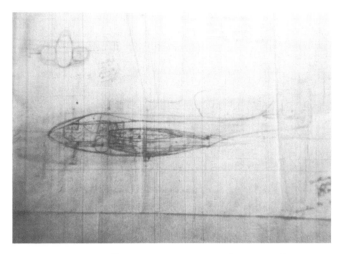

Evolution sketches of XP-59A done during the first weeks of design.(Drawing courtesy of JPA)

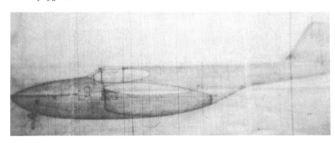

(Drawing courtesy of JPA)

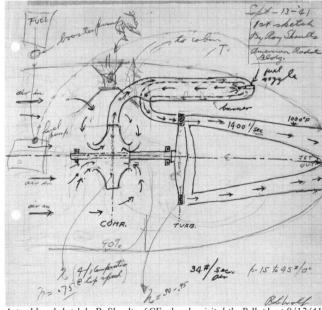

Actual hand sketch by R. Shoults of GE when he visited the Bell plant 9/13/41 to explain the "new propulsion machine".(Drawing courtesy of R. Wolf)

21

Shows wing attachment and wing design. (Photo courtesy of JPA)

This is in contrast to the British and German efforts in that the first jet airplanes produced by these countries were purely experimental in nature with no real hope or plan for production of these models.

As the project effort began to pick up momentum, it soon became necessary to increase the manpower level of the project and so in the main Bell plant, a strange thing began to occur — people suddenly began to disappear. Where these people had gone, what they were doing, or even if they still worked for Bell was a mystery to those who remained behind, and the now empty and vacant desks and drawing boards only served to add to the mystery. Of course, the people who were now working on the "X" airplane could not entirely end their social life, and when parties or a professional meeting took place and these "lost ones" made an appearance, they were subjected to the friendly cross-examination from their friends and ex-co-workers. The extent of the security finally reached the point where those working on the XP-59A were actually discouraged from participating in social affairs. The people working in the project not only had to refrain from telling their families what they were working on but the location of where they worked had to remain a secret. In the event of an emergency, the family could call a phone number that would ring a phone at the secret plant. The name of the party calling and their phone number was taken and this information was relayed to the employee, who could then return the call from another phone!

The all-metal, semi-monocoque fuselage of the XP-59A consisted of a spliced forward and aft section. The forward section was the principal component, with this section containing such items as the wing center section, the engines (which were housed in nacelles that were

Good view of engine intake and boundary layer bleed system to right of inlet.

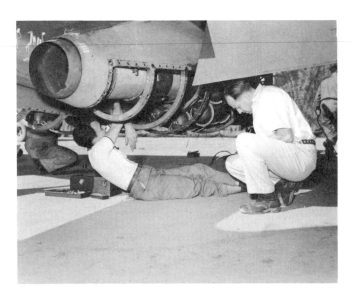

Al Bindig and Bob Wolf of Bell tinkering with thermocouples on tail pipe on first XP-59A. (Photo courtesy of J. Brown)

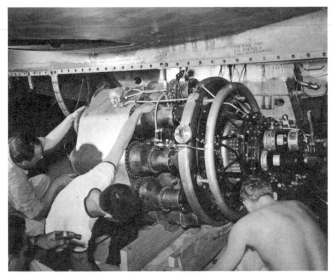

Al, The Welder, Ted Rogers and Ed Murphy. Note: hammer for final "Adjustments" as first I-A is installed. (Photo courtesy of J. Brown)

integral with the main fuselage), all engine accessories and controls, pilot compartment, radio equipment, the non-steerable nose landing gear and all flight control systems. The engines, which attached to the wing center section structure, were supported by three engine mounts located on the forward portion of the engine. Ready access to the engines and accessories was gained by the removal of the three sections of nacelle cowling. The pilot compartment was pressurized by using bleed air from the compressor of each engine to drive a tiny turbine air compressor to deliver fresh air to the cabin. The cabin glass was heated by using hot exhaust air from the left engine tail pipe. The gun compartment was heated by utilizing the air used to cool the rear engine bearings. Access to the cockpit was made through a side-hinged canopy.

The instrument panel was equipped with all the normal fighter type flight and engine instruments, and the general panel layout followed conventional design. However, the noticeable additions in the panel came in the form of an 18,000 rpm indicating tachometer and tail pipe temperature gauges. Later on, after the airplane had been flying for a while, a problem involving over temp of the engine bearings was encountered due to long tubes associated with visual oil sight gages and so bearing temperature gauges were incorporated as standard equipment. In flight, the airplane was found to be so vibration free, due to the smoothness of the jet engines, that it was necessary to install a vibrator (door bell) on the instrument panel so that the instruments would function properly and not stick due to the natural friction in the instrument mechanical linkage.

Even though the number one airplane was never fitted with any armament, it was designed from the outset to carry two type M4 37mm cannons, with 44 rounds of ammunition each, in the nose compartment. The second and third airplanes were so armed.

P-59A cockpit. Note: heads-up type - N - 3C gun site. (Photo courtesy of Aerophile)

Cockpit of XP-59A. Note: crank to right for lowering entire landing gear made from rachet wrench-type unit. Some 150-200 turns were required to accomplish pull and snug-up of landing gear. (Photo courtesy of Aerophile)

Excellent views of armament on P-59A- three 50 cal machine guns and one 37 mm cannon.(Photos courtesy of JPA)

Right side - P-59A cockpit interior with modified ratchet emergency landing crank snug-up device.(Photo courtesy of Aerophile)

Left side P-59A interior view, later model.(Photo courtesy of Aerophile)

Each wing was made up of an inner and outer panel with the inner panel attaching to the wing center section. The inner panel was built up on three spars consisting of the front beam, auxiliary beam and rear beam. The electrically-driven main landing gear retraction mechanism was located in the inner wing panel and it was attached to the auxiliary beam with the gear retracting inwards. The outer wing panel, carrying the aileron assembly, had only a front and rear beam with the inner wing auxiliary beam ending at the junction of the inner and outer panels. All of the fuel was carried in wing fuel tanks that consisted of four self-sealing cells in each wing for a total capacity of 290 U.S. gallons. The airfoil sections employed for the wing design were of the low drag laminar flow 66 series.

The ailerons were of monospar construction with fabric covering and they were actuated through a control system using bell cranks and push-pull tube assemblies. The aileron trim tabs, located on both ailerons, were cable operated.

The fabric covered flaps were located on the inner wing panels and each flap was raised and lowered through its individual gear box and actuating screw, both systems being driven by a 24 volt electric motor located in the fuselage.

The horizontal and vertical stabilizers were of conventional all metal construction. The rudder and elevators were of similar construction to the ailerons and they, too, were fabric covered. The use of fabric control surfaces might today seem to be a poor choice of materials for a jet airplane but it must be remembered that other airplanes of this period were capable of high speed performance and that they, too, were initially fitted with fabric surfaces. Actually, at this point (1941-

P-59-A - Excellent view showing details of canopy. (Photo courtesy of Aerophile)

P-59A weapons compartment shown from left - 37mm cannon with ammunition. .50 cal. ammunition boxes mount to rear of 37mm ammunition box. (Photo courtesy of Aerophile)

1942), the speeds had not progressed to the point where control surface distortion and/or failure of control surface fabric had become a problem. The fabric surfaces did eventually create a problem in the production P-59 Program and later models were modified to have metal covered surfaces.

One unexpected problem experienced with the fabric-covered elevators was the danger of burning or scorching them as a result of a "hot start" with the engines. The "hot start" could occur when accumulated raw kerosene in the tail pipe area was ignited during an engine start. To prevent damage to these surfaces, pilots were eventually instructed to keep the stick pulled back (up elevator) during engine starts!

Just a few short months after the initiation of the XP-59A Program, Bell submitted a quotation, on February 17, 1942, to the Army Air Force for 13 YP-59A airplanes to be used as service test articles. The Contract for procuring these airplanes was enacted as a supplement agreement to the original XP-59A Contract. The Contract called for 13 YP-59A airplanes, a static test airplane, wind tunnel models, spare parts, and data for a total cost, including fixed fee of $2,670,377.16 with this Contract being approved by the Secretary of War on March 26, 1942.

Both from an external and internal appearance, these airplanes, as originally built, closely resembled the "X" models because design changes between the two models were being held to a minimum in order that the transition from experimental to service test and eventually to the production airplane, would be as uninterrupted as possible. Initially, the only noticeable exterior difference between the two models was that the canopy on the "Y" models was of an aft sliding design, whereas the "X" airplanes had a hinged, side-opening canopy.

As the design of the service test models progressed, some questions arose regarding the suitability of the proposed armament for the airplanes but after considering several armament installations, the Army Air Force advised Bell that the first nine YP-59A airplanes should be armed with two 37mm cannons. After further considerations on the armament question, Bell was advised that the last four airplanes should be equipped with one 37mm cannon and three .50 calibre machine guns. These last four airplanes also differed in that they were to be provided with dropable auxiliary fuel tanks.

P-59A cockpit interior that was pressurized. Note: armor plate to rear of pilot's seat. (Photo courtesy of Aerophile)

XP-59A doing thrust testing late September 1942 at Muroc Dry Lake. (Photo courtesy of JPA)

P-59A at Bell factory - excellent view of drop tanks SN. 4422609. (Photo courtesy of JPA)

Cross sections tip-to-tail (see page 10)

25

On To Muroc Dry Lake

Muroc site built for this project - water tower - hangar and living quarters to right of hangar. (Photo courtesy of JPA)

Interior of hangar - GE engine shop was behind sliding door. (Photo courtesy of JPA)

Along with all the other problems occasioned by the extreme security measures of the project, it had been realized by the Army Air Corps that the flight testing of the jet airplane could not be carried out in the populated Buffalo area. Therefore, Colonel Chidlaw and Major Swofford made a tour of various sections of the country to determine a suitable location. After surveying the available sites, they selected the Army Air Force Muroc Bombing and Gunnery Range located on Rogers Dry Lake in eastern Kern County, California. <u>This site was later renamed Edwards Air Force Base on January 27, 1950</u>, in honor of Captain Glen W. Edwards, who was killed June 5, 1948 while flight-testing the Northrop YB-49 flying wing airplane. The jet flight test area, having now been established as the Materiel Command Flight Test Base, was located at the north end of the lake about five miles from the regular Army Air Force Base of Muroc. Later on in its career, this new area would sometimes be referred to as the Wright Field of the West, or as Muroc II.

It would have been hard to select a more ideal flying site, for the hard surface of Rogers Dry Lake afforded an almost unobstructed landing field encompassing approximately 65 square miles. Situated among the San Bernardino and Shadow Mountains, this area in the heart of the Mojave Desert, looked out across a vast barren wasteland of sand, tumbleweeds and an occasional grove of Joshua trees.

Bell was advised in mid-May 1942 that a test site had been selected and that the XP-59A airplanes would be tested at Muroc. It was at this point, that Larry Bell called in his Chief Test Pilot, Robert M. Stanley, and told him for the first time that Bell was actively engaged in the development of a jet-propelled airplane and that he should begin to establish a flight test program for the airplane. Stanley's aircraft experience dated back to 1931 when he first went to work for the Douglas Aircraft Company. Four years later, he received his Bachelor of Science Degree in Aeronautical Engineering from Cal Tech, with the next four years being spent as a Navy pilot. In 1939, he joined the United Aircraft Corporation as a test pilot and then joined Bell in 1940. Bob Stanley's task now became one of familiarizing himself with the airplane and its gas turbine engines and preparing the reorganization of this flight-research staff so that he could take several of these people some 2,000 miles to the California Desert, while still leaving sufficient personnel to handle the normal testing operations at Buffalo. So secret was the project, that many of the flight test people later sent to the Muroc site did not even know what airplane they were being sent to work on until they arrived and got their first look at the new airplane.

By the middle of July, the XP-59A airplanes were on schedule but Bell was being delayed due to slippage in the engine delivery schedule. Finally, on August 4, the type I-A engine arrived at Bell. The second engine followed shortly thereafter, and the final assembly of the number one airplane was then completed and the task of disassembling and crating it for shipment to Muroc began on September 10, 1942.

"Home sweet home" - for the crews. Note: swamp coolers in windows: an early form of air-conditioning using water evaporative cooling effect. (Photo courtesy of J. Brown)

Since the old Ford building had not originally been built to have airplanes on its second floor, it was necessary to make certain "structural changes" in the exterior of the building. A rather large hole was knocked in one of the brick walls so that the larger crated components of the airplane could be lowered to the ground and the waiting railroad cars. And so, at about two o'clock on the morning of September 12, the fuselage and wing crates were loaded and the journey began. At approximately eight o'clock on the morning of September 19, the XP-59A, Bell Model 27-1, along with the three General Electric personnel and five Military Guards that had accompanied the airplane, arrived at Muroc, California.

Unloading #2 or #3 XP-59A from a rail car 1942-43. (Photo courtesy of JPA)

Flying the XP-59A on rails as told by
Ted Rogers, a member of the GE Field Team

Early August saw engines, called Type I Superchargers for security reasons, being loaded into a boxcar under armed guard at Boston's South Station headed for Bell Aircraft, Buffalo, N.Y. Frank Burnham and I, selected to accompany the engines and supervise their installation in the airplane, spent the evening thoroughly briefing ourselves on the aircraft manual. It was the first time we had seen it.

The airplane itself, when we saw it next morning at the Main Street plant of Bell, was a mid-wing monoplane with wing loading so low it looked like a powered glider. It weighed about 9,000 pounds, had a span of 49 feet and a total length of 38 feet. The tricycle gear, built for jet engines, allowed it to sit low and level, giving excellent ground visibility. The tail section curved high to ensure clearing the jet wake.

August was spent fitting the engines in the airplane, re-routing fuel and air lines, rigging controls and completing the final assembly of the aircraft.

In early September, it was decided to ship the engines mounted in the plane to avoid delays of removal and re-installation. A stumbling block – a fear of damaging the bearings – we thought could be overcome by rotating the engines slowly while in transit. Somebody, of course, had to go with the plane to keep these engines rolling. We were determined to protect them at all costs, so with Angus McEachern, Lieut. Woolford, a Sergeant and two Privates from Wright Field added to our crew, we prepared for the "flight."

Midnight, September 12, '42, at the yards of the Niagara Power Company in Buffalo, Air Force guards patrolled the deserted area while a huge overhead crane lifted its precious cargo and set it down gently on the railroad flat cars. One crate contained the fuselage; another held the two wings. With previously prepared blocks, a gasoline powered air compressor was secured to the rear half of the flat car containing the fuselage, while a coil of copper tubing was unwound and connected in the interior of the crate. One could feel the

unspoken questions of the yard crew – what could possibly be in the crate to use compressed air? Some new explosive? A compressed air driven airplane?

It was just "Queenie." Actually, "Queenie" was at this particular time nameless. It was not until we had pulled the cowlings off several hundred times that some joker nicknamed her "Queenie" for the lady of burlesque fame.

We hastily completed coupling the air line and tried our system of propulsion. I was scared! I had proposed this method of rotating the engine. Here we were all set to take off for California. What if it didn't work? With a supreme show of self-confidence, we filled the gasoline tank, checked the engines for freeness and started the compressor. Meanwhile, the crates had been secured, and a safety rail placed around the open end of the car. We opened the valve feeding the air jets to the turbines – and the engines rolled! Climbing into the cockpit, I checked the engine speed at 400 rpm and observed that oil was flowing protectively to the bearings. The two flat cars and a combination mail and passenger cars for our home en route were coupled together, and with both engines purring we were off, coupled to the "Red Ball," California-bound fast freight.

Our "home" which we slowly put in order, was Vintage 1900. In the mail section we had six drums of gasoline, safety cans, filters and tools, plus an old ice chest stocked with what we considered the necessities of a "flight" to the coast for three persons. Someone had neglected our Army Air Corps companions. The passenger section of the car had several seats, on which we placed mattresses to make bunks. Our kitchen consisted of a Sterno stove and a case of canned heat. The salesman who sold us that stove has probably since made a fortune in Alaska selling refrigerators. It was just not intended to cook for seven and we discarded it after it proved unstable in "flight" – twice spilling our food the length of the car. The rest of the night was spent in securing the various pieces of equipment, as the jolting and swaying of the train proved necessary. It's no fun to hold down a one-ton compressor while fastening its ropes on a flat car traveling 60 mph or pouring gasoline into its ever-hungry mouth, while the cars hammer around a curve.

We lived through the first night, but mid-morning of next day the forward flat car bearings burned out. With incredible speed, a railway crane appeared, and within two hours the entire assembly had been changed. The rest of the day passed uneventfully until around 1:00 a.m., when I was awakened by loud voices and persistent shaking. Adjusting my eyes to the sparse light of the lantern, I saw uniforms and guns. Was this what they had warned me about – saboteurs! But no – more light and the bull-like voice of a Marine Sergeant convinced me that the trouble was not with saboteurs. A car of high explosive had been coupled to the front of our "home" and a squad of Marines accompanying it insisted we were in their accommodations. We compromised by letting them bed down in one end of the car while an armed truce prevailed.

After a sleepless night, we pulled into Kansas City where the Marines and most of our crew left during the time the car of explosives was shunted around. If you want a thrill ride down a railroad "hump" behind a car labeled in large red letters "High Explosives – Do Not Hump." We stood on the fuselage car while this was accomplished with a teeth-loosening jar. We soon convinced the railroad that we wanted no more of that, and the car with the Marines was relegated to the end of the train.

We did take advantage of the stop to run, in turns, to the nearest restaurant for a hot meal. You can imagine our surprise, Burnham's and mine, upon returning to find our car nowhere in sight!

A hectic search of the yards, assisted by a yard policeman who was convinced that we belonged in a nut house, finally located it. We were determined not to try that again. Enroute just about dusk after we had filled the compressor gas tank from a new drum, without warning it died. While the air hissed inexorably through the lines, we frantically tried to restart the compressor – useless. The ignition checked okay, so it must be the fuel. By frantic manipulation of the choke, it restarted just as the jet engines were coming to rest. The air pressure slowly climbed back up as we sighed with relief – then the engine quit again. This time we saved the day by blowing out the sediment bulb. This was only the beginning. Even though we replaced the dirty gas with that from another drum, we spent the whole night cleaning sediment and manipulating the choke and mixture needles during the off cycle of the compressor. We finally succeeded in removing all the dirt but the fuel system gave us frequent alarms all the rest of the trip.

Unloading more plane pieces. (Photo courtesy of JPA)

Tuesday and Wednesday we spent catching up on our sleep in relays, eating sandwiches fouled by gasoline and washing them down with sips of warm water. Twice we were parked in yards next to a carload of sheep! The food bill was low that day.

Thursday found us still plodding across country – engines purring. We stopped at Clovis, N.M., for water. Upon assurance the train would stand there for 20 minutes, we snatched a hot meal and raced back to it – all but Frank. He miscalculated, and we pulled out without him. Some miles further we swung into a siding to repair a car. A passenger train slowed as it passed, and Frank jumped off to rejoin us. Three hours in this barren land convinced us that we were the "foul ball" express. A protest wired to Wright Field convinced the railroad to cut off the car needing repairs and get us rolling.

On Friday we really set a pace across Arizona, halting only long enough to refuel and replenish water for the locomotive. Up through the mountains, cold and capped with snow, we climbed; then down into a green valley with palm trees lining the streets. We were in San Bernardino. Here we were switched from the main line and headed for Muroc. We passed our first peaceful night and early morning found us traveling across an unbroken vista of plain nothing, broken only by an occasional Joshua tree. Then Muroc! Off in the distance we could see the reflected sheen of a huge lake. The brakeman dispelled our impression. There was no lake; it was a mirage. Moving to a siding, we cut the air compressor. We were saddle sore and filthy as we climbed down from the first coast-to-coast "flight" of a jet airplane – six full days.

Unloading the first XP-59A at Muroc, September, 1942. (Photo courtesy of JPA)

Robert Stanley, Bell chief pilot, and Dr. Durand just prior to the first flight on October 2, 1942. (Photo courtesy of JPA)

Wendell Stuart, left, Joe Brown, top, from Bell and Jack Horn from GE with early XP-59A at Muroc. (Photo courtesy of J. Brown)

Bob Stanley had first arrived at the test site on August 20 to survey the progress being made on the construction of the hangar and barracks. Progress on the buildings was not as far along as had been hoped, and the Contractor held out little hope for having work completed by the middle of September. However, by the time the airplane arrived, the barracks were finished and the hangar was complete, except for a floor and the electrical wiring. The approaching arrival of the airplane necessitated the removal of the civilian construction personnel from the area, and Stanley and his crew had to make the finishing touches on the hangar. The first crew of Bell personnel had left Buffalo at eight A.M. on September 14, and consisted of 11 people, with this group arriving at Barstow, California September 17, 1942.

Conditions at the site were somewhat primitive with drinking water being obtained from a 200 foot deep well and water storage being maintained in a wooden water tank. A mess for feeding all personnel at the new area was set up and managed entirely by Bell personnel with the Army Air Force providing all of the cooking and kitchen utensils for the mess. Transportation at the base was provided by two company-owned station wagons that Bob Stanley had purchased in mid- August.

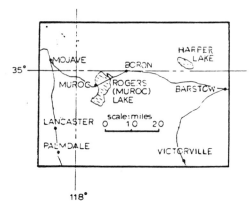

Map of the area in and around the Rogers Dry Lake. (Drawing courtesy of JPA)

The crated pieces of the airplane, after being unloaded from the train, were trucked on September 20 to the newly-built hangar at the test site where the Bell assembly team then began the task of reassembling the airplane and checking out the various systems. This work continued throughout the next week with the first installed engine run-up occurring on September 26. Both engines were successfully run through three five-minute run ups. The official target date for the first flight had been scheduled for October 2 and so a great deal of effort was being exerted by all members of the flight test team in order to meet this date. Larry Bell arrived at Muroc on September 30 in time to witness Bob Stanley make the initial taxi runs. After these initial trials, several "high speed taxi" runs were made for the purpose of general aircraft checkout and to obtain a feel for control surface effectiveness. During these runs "lift-off" actually occurred and based on the encouraging performance of the airplane, Bob Stanley wanted to go ahead and try for the first flight. However, since it was getting late in the day and not wishing to push their luck, Mr. Bell persuaded him to wait until the next day.

Then in the early afternoon of October 1, 1942, American aviation history was made when Stanley lifted the XP-59A from the Muroc Lake bed for the first jet flight. On this date, four flights were made, all with landing gear down and with the altitude being limited to about 100 feet.

Stanley's comments on the first flight have been recorded as follows:

> "Duration of flight: 30 minutes. Throttle was applied promptly and acceleration during take-off appeared quite satisfactory ... The first flight reached an altitude of approximately twenty-five feet."

The next day before Military and civilian observers who had come to witness the "official takeoff", Stanley made two more flights, one to 6,000 feet and the other to an altitude of 10,000 feet. The third flight of the day and the first by a U.S. Army Air Corps pilot, was made by Colonel Laurence C. Craigie who was also the Chief of the Aircraft Project Section at Wright Field. Colonels Keirn, Swofford and Chidlaw had actually already drawn straws to see who would be the first Military pilot to fly the XP-59A, however, at the time of the flight, all three of these men were absent from the Muroc area and so the honor fell to Colonel Craigie. Colonel Craigie was an old hand at the flying game, having joined the Army Air Service immediately after graduation from the United States Military Academy in 1923. The fourth and final flight of the day was then made by Mr. Stanley. Stanley was to stay on at the site until late in October when Larry Bell called him back to Buffalo. Bell test pilot, Frank H. "Bud" Kelley, Jr. then took over as the Representative-In-Charge for Bell on November 11.

Some of the people in attendance for the October 1 and October 2 flights were Harlan Poyer, E.P. Rhodes, Arthur L. Fornoff, R.A. Wolf and Herb Bowers of Bell; Roy Shoults and Don Warner from General Electric; Dr. W.F. Durand, NACA; and Major N.D. Heenan of the British Air Commission.

The XP-59A airplane, as first flown at Muroc, was finished in the standard U.S. Army Air Force camouflage scheme (Circa 1941-1942) of dark olive drab upper surfaces and gray lower surfaces. The national markings consisted of the blue circle with a white star and this marking was carried on the fuselage sides, upper left wing surface, and lower right wing surface. At the time of the first flight, no serial numbers or any other identifying marks were carried on the airplane.

October 2, 1942 Russ Ringle from Bell. Note: strings for air flow and temperature sensitive paint at exit of engines. (Photo courtesy of JPA)

Col. "Bill" Craigie, Dr.W. F. Durand of NACA and Larry Bell, president of Bell Aircraft.(Photo courtesy of JPA)

Col. Laurence "Bill" Craigie , first military pilot in the USA to fly a jet and Maj. Dodd in charge of T. Base Muroc, 1942. (Photo courtesy of J. Brown)

31

Following the October 2 flights, no more flights were made until October 30 due to repairs and modifications being carried out on the airplane.

On the last flight of October 2, the landing gear had failed to achieve full retraction (fortunately, however, it would fully extend and lock) and correcting this problem required the fabrication of new parts for the landing gear system. Two new I-A engines were received and installed in the airplane because at this time and for sometime to come, the engine life was anything but optimum. The serial numbers for the original Type I-A Supercharger engines used in the first XP-59A were no. 170121 left hand engine and no. 170131 right hand engine. A cutaway of an I-A engine no. 240215, is presently on display at the Air Force museum. It was during this period that the number one XP-59A received its unofficial nickname, "MISS FIRE". The name was given to the airplane at a time of some exasperation when one of the newly-installed engines repeatedly failed to start. The official name for the P-59A models, "Airacomet" did not come into usage until September 1943, when this name was selected from a list of names proposed by Bell employees who worked on the project.

(Photo courtesy of JPA)

The starting procedure for the I-A engines was actually quite simple. The first steps involved making certain that the fuel selector valves were switched to the proper tanks and that the stop cock fuel levers were set to the minimum position. The battery switch, general switch and engine switch were set on the "on" position, and when the electric starter had brought the engine up to about 1,200 rpm, the fuel stop cock was opened and the throttle was advanced to a half-way open position with the engine then firing in approximately five seconds. As soon as the engine fired, the throttle was returned to approximately a fourth-open setting. the only way to shut the engine down was to cut off the fuel supply to them by putting the stop cock fuel levers back to the "off" position.

Perhaps, at this point, it would be well to comment on a question dealing with the serial numbers for the XP-59A airplanes. The serial numbers assigned to the three "X" airplanes were 42-108784, 42-108785, and 42-108786. However, the serial numbers given to the 13 service test "Y" models were 42-108771 through 42-108783 and, thus, from the serial numbering sequence it is seen that the "Y" models have lower numbers than the "X" models. Examination of photographs of the XP-59A airplanes shows that initially, none of the "X" airplanes carried any serial numbers on their vertical stabilizer. It is, therefore, by conjecture that because of the special secret classification given to the jet propulsion project, that the three "X" airplanes were not even originally assigned serial numbers and that only after the project classification was reduced to "Secret" in May 1943, were serial numbers assigned and in the security shuffle the "Y" models were assigned serial numbers first.

YP-59A - Boundary layer bleed slot can be seen well at engine inlet — P- static tube has been moved to rudder. Note squared-off wing tips and ventral fuselage fin. (Photo courtesy of J. Brown)

PILOT'S REPORT

Place: **Materiel Center Flight Test Base**   Flight #2

Pilot: **Robert M. Stanley**

Weather: **Calm, C.A.V.U., hot**

Purpose: **Shakedown Flight**

Changes Since Last Flight: -- Light hatch installed, no observer
or ballast
      26.4 wheels up
C.G. ____ 27.4 wheels down   Gross Weight 10,089 Pounds   Time Take-Off 12:53P
      %M.A.C.

1. After considerable run as a result of the reduced thrust and heavy load, the airplane made a gentle take-off and after approximately 300 feet had been obtained the wheels were retracted. The latter did not go completely closed, The cockpit switch was returned to neutral to avoid damage to the landing gear motor.

2. After take-off the engine power rose to 15,500 r.p.m. and was throttled back to cruising figure of 15,000 which occurred with throttle approximately one-half open as judged by throttle quadrant position.

3. The landing gear horn blew throughout the flight while the wheels were retracted.

4. The airplane was climbed leisurely to 6,000 feet. Stalls were made with flaps up and flaps down. The stalling speed appeared to be about 80 indicated m.p.h., flaps down. The flaps up stall was not quite fully stalled.

5. A maximum speed of 160 indicated m.p.h. was attained.

6. The flight was terminated due to faulty action of the right engine's electric oil-pressure gauge. The trouble has been traced to a faulty electric transmitter and does not indicate faulty lubrication.

7. All temperatures were well within their maxima through the flight.

8. Fuel consumption appeared to be about 150 gallons per hour per engine.

9. The engines do not idle sufficiently slowly to facilitate landing in a small field. The landing itself is easily executed and not associated with any special technique.

Form C1-7

Pilot log official first flight, October 2, 1942. (Courtesy of JPA)

PILOT'S REPORT NO. 2 (CONT'D)

10. The heat in the cockpit is intense and is undoubtedly due to faulty ventilation control.

11. The change in trim due to change in power is entirely unnoticeable. The change in trim due to landing gear and flap operation is exceedingly mild. At the speed reported above, the airplane's handling qualities are excellent and all controls seem well coordinated. Steep turns were made in both directions and although the rate of roll is not high the forces are quite normal for the speed involved.

12. Approximately 52% of the design thrust of 1,640 lbs./engine was available from L.H. engine #170121 and from R.H. engine #170131 during this flight.

Total Flight Time To Date   50 Minutes

PILOT'S REPORT

Place: Materiel Center Flight Test Base   Flight #4

Pilot: Colonel L. C. Craigie

Weather: Calm, C.A.V.U., hot

Purpose: Familiarization

Changes Since Last Flight: Cut right vent line, installed hatch

    26.4 wheels down
C.G. 27.4 wheels up   % M.A.C.   Gross Weight 10,089 Pounds   Time Take-Off 5:20PM

1. The airplane was flown by Colonel Craigie for purposes of familiarization. The cockpit hatch was installed this flight.

Total Flight Time To Date   1 Hr, 35 Min.

FORM EA-1

First Military Pilot (Courtesy of JPA)

STATIC THRUST INVESTIGATION

THRUST = R - F

F = STATIC FRICTION = 175 $^{\#}$

Thrust log sheet, September 30, 1942. (Courtesy of JPA)

Getting Down To Business

"Superman" observer seat added at Muroc on XP-59A. (Photo courtesy of Aerophile)

During the month of October the first airplane underwent modification so that an observer could be carried in the nose section. This modification consisted of mounting a standard airplane seat and an instrument panel in the area that was normally to be the gun compartment. A 20 inch hole was then cut in the upper fuselage skin, some rubber combing and a small Plexiglas windshield were added and the result was the world's first two-seated jet airplane. The purpose of this modification, of course, was to enable an observer to go along and record the much-needed flight data. When flying with the number one airplane was finally resumed on October 30, 1942, Mr. E. P. Rhodes, the Bell project engineer for the XP-59A, went along as the first observer.

In these early days almost all of the flight test data was taken by the pilot reading his instruments and radioing the information back to the ground, or he could attempt to jot the information down on a pad of paper while he continued to fly the airplane. Because of the many readings required for the new jet engines, the added cockpit for the observer on the XP-59A was a real asset. Later on in the program Brown Recorders were installed in the airplane to record data and an instrument panel was installed in the aft fuselage section with this panel then being photographed during flight so as to obtain a continuous data record throughout the test.

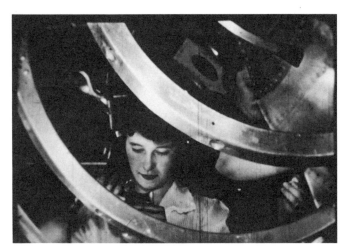

Rosie the riveter at Bell's New York assembly plant for P-59's. (Photo courtesy of JPA)

Lynn Bldg 1-29 assembly area for I-16 production models circa 1944.(Photo courtesy of JPA)

Meanwhile, back at the factory, work had continued on the other two XP-59A airplanes, so that by the end of October the second airplane, 27-2, was complete except for engine installation and landing gear retraction system, and assembly on the third airplane, 27-3, was approximately 80 percent complete. General Electric was unable to meet the engine delivery schedule for the second airplane, and so when fabrication was completed, it was shipped on to Muroc without engines. The wing panels arrived on December 27, followed by the fuselage on January 4, 1943, but the end of January found it still at Muroc without engines. The engines finally arrived in the early part of February and the first flight of the number two airplane took place on February 15, 1943, with Frank Kelley at the controls. The first flight of this plane proved to be far from routine. No sooner had Kelley taken off than the cabin defroster malfunctioned, with the result that the cockpit filled with smoke. Reacting quickly to the situation he made a tight turn, began a landing approach, cut the engines and then proceeded to make a dead stick landing. No permanent damage was done to the plane and further flights were resumed on a regular schedule the next day. As the flight program continued, the practice of making dead stick landings actually became rather routine. This situation came about as a result of the combination of three factors; limited endurance of the airplane, a low wing loading and the great expanse of space available at Muroc. To make full use of these factors the pilots sometimes would fly the airplanes until they ran out of fuel and then peacefully glide back to the base.

The same problem of delayed engine delivery confronted the third airplane and it was shipped, without engines, from the Main Street plant on February 5, 1943. This airplane arrived at the site on February 21,

Bell Assembly Plant for P-59s.(Photo courtesy of JPA)

Outside lineup of P-59s at Bell plant. (Photo courtesy of JPA)

1943, but due to the lack of engines and the work and modifications being carried out on the first two, it was not immediately assembled.

The problem of engine delivery slippage was certainly not a new one, for as early as October 30, 1942, Colonel Swofford had stressed the fact to Colonel Chidlaw that little progress could be made on the XP-59A flight test program until sufficient engines were available at the test site. The need for additional engines was necessary because engine inspections would be constantly interrupting the test program. In all fairness to General Electric, it must be remembered that they were involved in producing a truly revolutionary, and to a large degree, untried, type of powerplant, and the problems being experienced with the I-A engines were merely the growing pains of a new piece of equipment.

The work on the Y model design had also progressed rapidly so that by the middle of August 1942 the engineering on the first nine airplanes was almost complete. A review of the progress on the airplanes was made by newly-promoted Colonel Swofford, in late October, and at this time he estimated that the first YP-59A could not be delivered before February 28, 1943. Because of various problems, this anticipated date came and went without the delivery of the Y model.

The first YP-59A, 27-4, was finally delivered to Muroc on June 12, 1943, quickly followed by the arrival of the second YP-59A, 27-5, on June 22, 1943. The delivery of the Y airplanes was behind schedule because of interference from the P-63 program, delay in the receipt of parts, changes that were necessary because of failures in the static test airplane and changes that had to be made to the canopy emergency release mechanism. Even after

Earl Fisher, Bell inspector with Frank "Bud" Kelley. Bells follow on chief test pilot at Muroc. Earl once got flipped over by the jet exhaust when he got too close during a ground run-up. (Photo courtesy of J. Brown)

Capt. Fred M. Trapnell, first Navy jet pilot with Joe Brown, Bell crew chief, April 21, 1943. Note hinged canopy on this XP-59A was sliding on later P models. (Photo courtesy of J. Brown)

Excellent view of P-59A at New York plant.(Photo courtesy of JPA)

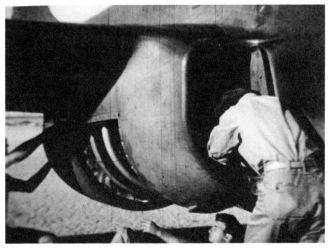

Muroc Dry Lake early days. (Photo courtesy of J. Brown)

Moving the second XP-59A to a new site due to flooding of "Dry" Lake. Note: fake propeller made by Joe Brown standing second from left and Lt. B. Van Doren in foreground. (Photo courtesy of J. Brown)

the first two airplanes were delivered to Muroc their initial flights were delayed because of further modifications being made to the canopy release and to the ailerons. The first flight of the YP-59A's 27-4 and 27-5 took place on September 15 and August 18, 1943, respectively. Still a further problem associated with the first Y models delivered to Muroc was that they lacked the more powerful I-16 engine that had been promised for them. The lack of the I-16 engines at the desired time had been anticipated by Bell and they had therefore installed smaller tail pipes on the first six airplanes so that either the I-A or I-14B engines could be installed without problems. Performance flight tests were carried out on the second YP-59A, 27-5, in December 1943. This airplane was powered with the I-A engines and since its configuration was the same as the X airplanes, its performance is then representative of both the X and Y models. The maximum true air speed attained was 389 miles per hour at an altitude of 35,160 feet and a gross weight of approximately 8,900 pounds. At maximum rpm (16,500) this speed fell to about 350 miles per hour at sea level. Minimum time to climb to 30,000 feet was 18.82 minutes. Four other YP-59A airplanes were eventually flown at the Muroc site with Nos. 27-7, 27-8, 27-9 and 27-10 being delivered on October 7, 26, November 1 and 16, 1943, respectively.

The last one of these YP-59A airplanes delivered 27-10, was eventually modified to have a second open seat

cockpit, in a manner similar to the original XP-59A. Still another YP-59A was modified to have the second cockpit, this airplane, 27-16, named the "Mystic Mistress", was used as the "Mother" plane during the development of radio control equipment for drone airplanes in late 1944 and early 1945. The original drone or "robot" airplane used in this program was also a YP-59A, 27-13. However, on March 23, 1945 this airplane was completely destroyed during a radio-controlled takeoff. After this accident, a production P-59B-1, 44-22633, named the "Reluctant Robot", was used as the "robot" airplane for the remainder of the program. "The Mystic Mistress" was to gain a further distinction when it was used to carry the first air mail to be flown by a jet airplane.

Prior to its conversion to a two seater, the YP-59A airplane, 27-16, was used in gunnery tests to determine its suitability as a gun platform. These tests were carried out in April 1944 with firing tests of the three .50 caliber machine guns made at speeds varying from 220 mph to 340 mph. During this series of tests the 37mm cannon was not fired because of the problem of attempting to simultaneously hit a deflecting target with the machine guns and cannon. As a result of these tests, it was concluded that, as tested, the YP-59A airplane was unsatisfactory as a gun platform because of its poor directional stability at speeds above 290 mph.

40

Along with all the other problems normally expected with a new airplane and powerplant, it was unfortunate for the XP-59A program that heavy rains came to the usually dry California desert in late January 1943, with the resulting flooding of the lake bed preventing further flight testing of the airplane. However, while waiting for the lake surface to dry out, the time was utilized to conduct ground tests on the engines in an attempt to solve the critical problem of engine bearing over-heating that had developed during the flight tests. The results of these ground tests indicated that the over-heating of the bearings was apparently the result of excessive bearing tolerances.

The bad weather continued through February with the further reports indicating that more rain could be expected. Since the urgency of the project required that flight testing should resume as soon as possible, it was then necessary to locate an alternate flying area. It was quickly discovered that an area was available at an auxiliary air field, Hawes Field, of the Victorville glider program. The Victorville Air Base (later George Air Force Base) was located about 35 miles from the Muroc site. Because of this need, General Carroll issued a directive that permitted flights from another location, and so on March 10, 1943, the number two XP-59A was towed down a public highway for approximately 35 miles to Hawes Field. To maintain the security of the airplane for this trip, the entire center section of the fuselage and most of the nose section was wrapped in canvas and in addition, a dummy four-bladed propeller was fitted on the nose. During this move the highway was briefly closed to public travel.

The number one XP-59A was left at the Muroc site where work continued on the various modifications and revisions required on this airplane.

After making one flight from Hawes Field, on March 11, it was decided that this base was unsatisfactory from the standpoint of security. Therefore, another move was made, about March 15, to Harpers Lake, located almost due north of the Victorville base. This area proved to be adequate for flight testing even though it made the overall operations somewhat difficult. This temporary site was located about 42 miles from the main base at Muroc and therefore it was very inconvenient to transport all the personnel to and from this base daily. In addition, it was now necessary to maintain a considerable amount of supplies at this auxiliary base, and it was also necessary to provide a noon-day meal for the personnel.

The Harpers Lake site was used until April 7, when improved surface conditions of Rogers Dry Lake permitted the return of the flight test program. The number two airplane was then flown back, and the temporary Harpers site was disbanded much to the relief of all involved.

The GE crew: Frank Burnham, Ed Tritle, Roy Shoults, Ted Rogers and Angus McEachern, October 2, 1942.(Photo courtesy of J. Brown)

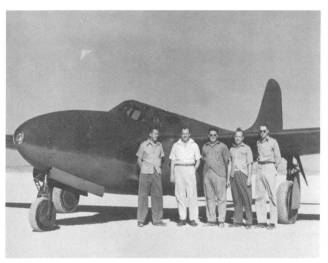

Bell's design team: H. Poyer, R. Wolf, E. Rhodes, Jim Limage and H. Bowers, five of the "Secret 6", before the first flight - Brian Sparks is missing.(Photo courtesy of R. Wolf)

Top Brass: Bob Stanley, Gen. Chidlaw, Col. Don Keirn, Col. Ralph Swofford and Larry Bell.(Photo courtesy of R.Wolf)

41

By April 11, 1943 the first XP-59A had made 30 flights for a total flying time of only 15 1/4 hours, while the second airplane had made 24 flights and acquired 13 3/4 hours of flight time. The third airplane had not yet been flown. During the remaining part of April the flight testing began to gather some momentum, so that by the 25th of the month the number one airplane had a total of 20 hours, 10 minutes, the number two plane a total of 17 hours, 2 minutes, and the third XP-59A had finally flown for a total flight time of one hour, three minutes. During the April-May period, approximately 67 flights were made covering such areas as glide tests, speed-power calibrations, landing gear tests and performance investigations. From the first flight of the number one airplane, on October 1, 1942, through January 1943, about 15 hours of flying time had been accumulated and all of this time was on the first XP-59A. For the first month of its flying existence, October 1942, the airplane flew a total of 5 hours, 45 minutes. In November it flew only 3 hours, 40 minutes. In December no flights were made at all and in January 1943, the airplane was flown 5 hours, 15 minutes. This rather low number of flight hours was not due to any serious problems associated with the airplane, but rather, it was the result of the constant tinkering, maintenance and troubleshooting of this new form of propulsion.

The problem of engine surge at high altitudes was a characteristic of the W.2B engine, and even though the W.2B was a British design and already well into the development stage when General Electric first received the drawings, it fell to General Electric and Bell to first encounter and then solve this problem. This situation occurred because the XP-59A flew some 10 months before its contemporary, the F.9/40. The order for the F.9/40 had been placed by the British Ministry of Aircraft Production on February 7, 1941. However, the first taxiing trials of the airplane were not made until March 5, 1943. When this first flight of the F.9/40 did occur, the airplane was powered by a Halford H.1 engine which also employed a centrifugal single sided compressor. Its combustion system was of a straight-through design rather than the reverse-flow of the Whittle engine. The first flight of an F.9/40 airplane powered by a Whittle-type engine (W.2B/23) did not take place until July 24, 1943.

Out of the many difficulties and problems of the I-A engine came the necessary experience and knowledge required to design the newer and better jet engines that General Electric would produce in the years to come. As advances were made in engine design, I-A units in the three XP-59A models were eventually replaced by General Electric I-14B engines. The I-14 engine was very similar to the I-A design but it featured improvements in the casing design, an improved turbine wheel (based on the design of the W.2500) and new combustion liners. The I-14 engine made its first run-up at the General Electric plant in February 1943, delivering some 1,400 pounds of thrust.

In preparation for the Navy's participation in the jet aircraft field, Captain Frederick M. Trapnell, Chief of Flight Test for the Bureau of Aeronautics, became the first Naval aviator to fly a jet when he made a flight in the number one XP-59A at Muroc on April 21, 1943. Captain Trapnell had been ordered to Muroc to undertake somewhat of a mysterious project and it was during the trip that he was first briefed on the nature of the XP-59A project and on the jet propulsion engines that powered it. Recalling this early flight, Admiral Trapnell, U.S.N. Ret., provided the following remarks some 25 years ago:

"In ground run-ups the jet was very impressive for its unusual nose and the 'blow-torch' slipstream, but the aircraft was obviously a very gentle type of high-altitude fighter with low wing-loading. It was a great surprise to find that the thing was very quiet and smooth from the pilot's point of view. During takeoff the rattling of the landing gear was audible and the general impression was that of a glider. The XP-59 was comparatively low-powered and this was apparent from the shallow climb-out. Its performance was, at first, distinctly unimpressive – long takeoff and slow rate of climb"

Captain Trapnell found himself in a rather interesting situation:

"I found myself in a group discussing rumors then emanating from Europe, of a weird and wonderful means of propulsion – without a propeller. The discussion became quite intense and very inaccurate, to say the least. I was supposed to be the most knowledgeable of those present but I had to sit silent and act dumb. I couldn't say that I not only knew about it but had flown one. I was forbidden to say a word."

In November 1943, the Navy received its first jet airplanes when two YP-59A's, 27-11 and 27-12 were shipped to the Naval Air Station at Patuxent River, Maryland where they were to be flight tested. In late 1945 the Navy was to receive three production P-59B-1 airplanes, 44-22651, 44-22657 and 44-22658 with these three airplanes also being evaluated at Patuxent River.

Several "firsts" were naturally associated with this jet project and another of these was the precedent set by Colonel Keirn on June 16, 1943, when he removed the propeller blades from the insignia worn on his uniform to the cheers of the crew who had asked him when he was going to jettison them. He also gave verbal permission for Army Air Force personnel who were associated with the airplane to remove the now "outdated" props from their insignias.

The 412th fighter group - 1st jet squadron of the 4th Air Force - activated in late November of 1943 at Muroc, California, under the direction of Col. Homer A. Boushey. (Photo Courtesy of JPA)

Still another "first" but this time of a more humorous vein, at least to all but the involved party, occurred when one of the Bell crew walked into the jet exhaust. The following quote is from the Bell flight test log of February 10, 1944:

> "On this date, Bell inspector E. F. Fisher, weighing 200 pounds, walked into the jet approximately four feet behind the nozzle while the aircraft was operating at rated power. It lifted him approximately 3 feet in the air, tumbled him end over end approximately 3 times, and he made a face-down landing on the concrete approximately 25 feet behind the nozzle exit. No substantial injuries were sustained other than brush burns obtained upon contact with the concrete surface."

More "Firsts", the "X" models continued to be flown at Muroc at a regular pace so that by October 8, 1943 the number two plane had accumulated 53 hours, 35 minutes with number three logging 42 hours, 5 minutes of flight time by November 17, 1943. It was during this period of testing that Bell test pilot, Jack Woolams, reached an altitude of 45,765 feet in number two on July 14, 1943. Several months later, on December 15, 1943, Woolams established a new unofficial American altitude record for single place aircraft when he reached an altitude of 47,600 feet while flying a YP-59A, 27-4.

The first Army Air Force jet-equipped unit was the 412th Fighter Group of the Fourth Air Force. The 412th was activated in late November 1943 at Muroc under the direction of Colonel Homer A. Boushey. Colonel Boushey was no newcomer to pioneering aviation projects, for on August 6, 1941 Captain Boushey made the first rocket-powered flight in this country when he piloted a rocket-powered Ercoupe in a brief flight at March Field, California. Originally, the Fourth Air Force furnished about 20 enlisted mechanics and one engineering officer so that this group could be trained in the maintenance and operational care of the jet airplanes. The group was also to serve as a nucleus for the training of pilots and other personnel who would be serving with units that would be equipped with jet airplanes.

The third YP-59A, Bell S/N 27-6, AAF 42-108773, became an international traveler when the crated airplane was shipped directly from the Bell factory to the RAF field at Moreton Valance, England. This shipment left the plant on or about September 13, 1943 and the fuselage crate arrived at Moreton Valance on September 26 with the crated wings arriving the next day. The Moreton Valance facility has been selected because it offered the necessary equipment and personnel for assembly, and since Gloster shared the field with the RAF, a high degree of security could also be maintained at this location. The assembly of the airplane was carried out by a joint RAF crew and Gloster Aircraft experimental group personnel under the direction of Mr. Charles Crosser and Frank Burnham of General Electric and "Doc" Meshako of Bell. Kelley, now Bell's deputy chief test pilot, had accompanied the other three Americans to England and when the airplane had been assembled and checked out, he made the first flight in it on September 28, 1943. This flight was witnessed by Mr. M. Daunt, Chief Test Pilot for Gloster, Mr. John Grierson, Assistant Chief Test Pilot for Gloster and Wing Commander H. J. Wilson, RAF. After this demonstration flight, the airplane was turned over to the RAF for their use and evaluation.

On November 5, Wing Commander Wilson flew the airplane from Moreton Valance to Farnborough, where the flight test program on the airplane was to be conducted by "T" Flight to which the aircraft was attached. From December 1943 through January 1944 the airplane made nine flights totalling 5 hours, 10 minutes, with the pilots for these flights being W/Cdr Wilson, S/Ldr DBS Davie and S/Ldr Moloney. At the end of January the engines were pulled and sent away for overhaul, and it was April 1944 before the plane again flew. When flying did resume the pilots were Wilson and Moloney and six flights for a total flight time

43

of 4 hours, 24 minutes were made from April 17 through April 26. After these flights, the engines were again apparently removed for overhaul and after this point no further efforts on the airplane were undertaken. The British Air Commission, on November 30, 1944, officially advised the AAF that the anticipated test program for the airplane could not be completed because of more urgent operational and development work. Since the storage of the plane was taking up needed space, they advised that it would either have to be stored in England at a maintenance unit or returned to the United States, and they requested that the AAF make a decision on this matter. The Air Technical Service Command (ATSC) that had control over this phase requested that the British make arrangements to return the airplane to Wright Field. Consequently, by late June 1945, the airplane had been received at the Foreign Equipment Branch, Vandalia, Ohio (naturally, since the airplane was now a British Type!) and from there it was sent to the NACA laboratory at Cleveland, Ohio for modifications.

When the airplane was first shipped from Bell it was painted in the standard AAF colors and markings. The British repainted it with their typical camouflage scheme of gray and green with all the undersurfaces being painted a bright yellow. British national markings and a British serial number, RJ 362/G, were also applied. The RAF name that was given to the YP-59A was "TOLL-GATE."

In 1966 Mr. R. C. Wright, Chief Librarian at Farnborough provided several very interesting notes on this particular airplane. Part of the material that he provided was in the form of extracts from a diary that was kept by "T" Flight. This information is repeated here because it so clearly points out some of the problems the British experienced, plus an excellent example of British humor:

"April 1944. The Bell has been gaily dropping static vents on the unsuspecting citizens of Farnborough and/or Fleet: We'll have to think of a new knot that won't break. The engines also have been removed now and as yet we know not where the new ones are coming from.

"May 1944. The Bell is still minus engines and nobody seems to be very interested in the poor thing.

"June 1944. The Bell, after having some 200 odd modifications applied to it, is to be sent back to America, and will probably never fly again here.

"July 1944. Bell still here, but in bits and has been hidden away in a Bersoneau hangar.

"August 1944. The Bell is going to Rolls - Royce. We wish them joy - they know not what they have taken on. We have done only 60 of the outstanding modifications on it."

Originally the British Air Commission had requested the six YP-59A airplanes be allocated to them, however, after considering this request, it was decided that two of the Y airplanes could be furnished without any serious damage occurring to the AAF program. This initial request was made in early July 1943 and resulted in the shipment of the first Y model, 27-6. However, by December 1943 a further agreement was reached whereby a production P-59A airplane was to be sent to England instead of a second YP-59A. Having received the Y airplane and then encountering so many varied problems on it must have caused the British to reconsider this agreement, for in August 1944 they advised the Army Air Force that they no longer really desired to have one of the production airplanes shipped to them!

In exchange for the Y airplane sent to them, and in fulfillment of General Arnold's original request, they eventually sent one of their jet airplanes to the United States. The airplane that was sent was the first production Meteor I, S/N EE 210, which was shipped from England in early February 1944. The pilot for the first flight of this airplane at Muroc, on April 15, 1944, was British test pilot John Grierson. Back in April 1943, Wing Commander Wilson of the Royal Air Force had traveled to Muroc and there he made a flight in the number one XP-59A to become the first British pilot to fly the American jet.

Shortly after Kelley left Muroc, another Bell test pilot, Alvin M. (Tex) Johnston, arrived on September 25, to help Jack Woolams with the flight test program. Johnston remained at the site through the middle of November 1943, and returned to Muroc again on December 31, 1943 to take over the duties of Representative-In-Charge to relieve Woolams, enabling Jack to return to Buffalo to handle more pressing duties there. On January 2, 1944, Johnston was joined by another Bell pilot, R. J. O'Gorman.

Due to the fact that the three "X" airplanes were used primarily to solve engine programs, the first army official performance tests of the XP59A airplane were made in October 1943 on an I-16 - powered YP-59A. Even then, the performance tests could not be completed because of engine surge problems that limited flights to a maximum altitude of 20,000 feet.

The I-16 was an improved version of the basic I-A design with the engine developing 1,650 pounds of thrust at 16, 500 rpm. This engine was the first satisfactory American turbojet to be released for quantity production, and it was also the first engine to be given a "J" designation when it became the J31. Though the I-16 was a greatly improved model (but still a Whittle type), it was still necessary in most cases to prematurely overhaul one before it reached the allowable total time between overhauls of 50 hours.

All of the test area in and around the north end of the lake was in a restricted air zone because of the classified projects being carried out there. However,

Trade mark derby hats worn by the test group at Muroc. (Photo courtesy of J. Brown)

Jack Woolams, test pilot for Bell, would later be killed in the Thompson Trophy race of 1946 in the Cobra I. (Photo courtesy of JPA)

every now and then, curiosity would overcome better judgment, and some of the P-38 pilots flying out of the Lockheed plant at Burbank, would sneak over for a quick look around. On one such visit, a P-38 pilot suddenly found an XP-59A on his tail with all appearances indicating that the jet was going to shoot him down, being in a restricted section, and with discretion winning over valor, the P-38 headed back across the mountains at a high rate of speed! Howard Hughes once visited Muroc to fly the XP-59A but the crew faked an engine problem so he would not get to use "their" special bird just for fun.

Still other flying visitors came to the secret test area, this time from the Muroc Army Air Corps Base where new pilots were acquiring their first 20 hours in the P-38. Briefs were given to these pilots not to fly "over" the lake. However, in mid-June of 1943, Lt. Royal D. Frey was flying "near' the end of the lake when he saw an airplane take off from the small cluster of buildings. Though too high to make out any details, he watched as the airplane continued its takeoff and climb. As the airplane began to climb out, its shadow was cast against the almost pure white surface of the dry lake bed below, and as he watched this shadow, he could see the shadow airplane had a long trail of "smoke" coming from it and yet from the real airplane there was no trace of this. In retrospect, what he probably saw was the shadow cast by the heat waves from the jet engines. After its takeoff, he lost sight of the airplane until several minutes later when it suddenly and rapidly passed by him in a steep rolling climb. However, this brief encounter was enough to let him see that this airplane had no propellers.

Returning to the base, he reported the sighting of this propellerless airplane to the other pilots, but being men of logic, they assured him that he must be "drunk" since it was obvious that an airplane could not fly without a propeller. Realizing the error of his way, he dismissed the matter from his mind until several months later, when news of the jet airplane was released, and then he knew that he had witnessed a flight of one of these airplanes. The airplane he saw was probably the number two or three plane during an aileron response test to check out some newly-designed ailerons.

When a group of people must work long hours and under adverse conditions, it is not unusual for them to adopt a trademark, and such was true for the Bell crew. As their trademark they took to wearing black derby hats, and it is reported that to see a group dressed in desert togs and black derby hats bowling or drinking at some bar was indeed a sight to behold.

On still another flying encounter, Jack Woolams used his derby hat as part of a practical joke. Army Air Force planes were always flying somewhere in the area, and so he had decided to have a little fun at their expense. The equipment he needed, in addition to his hat, was a Halloween mask and a P-59. One day a flight of Army fighters were peacefully flying along when suddenly they were joined by another airplane. Imagine their surprise when they saw that this airplane had no propellers, but the real shock came when they saw that the pilot of this strange new airplane was a cigar-smoking, black derby hat-wearing – gorilla!

45

The extreme secrecy of the jet project had from time to time proved troublesome, however, on one occasion at least, this secrecy requirement presented somewhat of an actual hazard. The situation developed on September 24, 1943 during a photographic mission with another aircraft. When the two airplanes had taken off the weather was clear, but abruptly and almost without warning, a terrific sandstorm came up out of the east. At the end of their mission and with the XP-59A beginning to run short of fuel, it was necessary to head for home base. Arriving over the area of the base, the pilots found the ground completely obliterated. So severe was the sandstorm that the accompanying aircraft proceeded directly on to Burbank for a landing. However, Woolams flying the classified XP-59A had no other choice but to chance a landing, and so it was necessary to make an instrument landing during the height of the storm, fortunately, without mishap.

Jack Woolams had won his wings at Kelly Field, Texas in June 1938 and after serving with the 79th Pursuit Squadron he returned to the University of Chicago to get his degree. Graduating in June 1941, he joined Bell as a test pilot. His work with the XP-59A was just a preview of things to come, for by 1946 he had reached the position of Chief Test Pilot for Bell and was preparing to be the first man to reach supersonic speeds in the new Bell XS-1 rocket-plane. However, Jack Woolams was to meet his death on August 30, 1946 in the tragic crash of the Thompson Trophy racer, Cobra I.

Though much of the flight time was being spent on power plant experimentation, it soon became apparent that several problems existed with the airplane itself. One of the problems that was becoming obvious was that the airplanes were underpowered even when the engines were operating at peak performance. The need of a weight reduction study to help solve this problem was even more apparent when one considered the fact that the power-plant installation in the XP-59A was about 25% less in weight than that in the P-39, yet the gross weight of the XP-59A was about 25% more than the P-39 — being approximately 10,300 pounds. Mechanical problems were encountered with the 37mm cannons, the pressure cabin and the ailerons and flaps. Aerodynamic problems appeared in the combined form of poor spin characteristics and a low level of directional stability.

The spin tests on the XP-59A airplanes were started late in December 1943 with Woolams serving as the test pilot. However, it was quickly discovered that it was extremely difficult to recover from a spin, and so the tests were postponed until a fix could be developed. This problem was not unexpected because in March

A. McEachern, Joe Brown, Jim George, Lt. Von Doren, Earl Leithliter, UK, Bob Wheelock, Wendel Stuart and Jack Russell's back - 1942 Muroc test site.

46

1943 Bell had received the NACA reports on the YP-59A spin model that had been tested in the NACA vertical spin tunnel and from the results of these model tests. It appeared that the airplane was just marginal in regards to spin recovery. Bell had also been unable to decide upon any practical changes that could be made to the airplane to improve its spin characteristics. However, after reviewing the same NACA model spin data, the Engineering Division at Wright Field stated that even though the results indicated marginal recovery, it was felt that the spin tests could be performed on the full scale airplane without undue risk. After the problem was encountered with the actual airplane, it was then necessary to add a ventral fin in order to produce a satisfactory spin and recovery. With this modification being made, the spin tests were completed on February 11, 1944 with Jack Woolams again flying all of this test program.

In order to evaluate the military potential of the production P-59A-1 airplanes, it was necessary to carry out the accelerated service tests, operational tests and tactical suitability tests using the Y model airplanes equipped with the I-16 engines. Three YP-59A airplanes were used for these tests, 27-5, 27-7 and 27-9. Testing on these programs began February 5, 1944 with personnel from the Air Forces Board, Army Air Force Proving Ground Command and Materiel Command cooperating on the efforts. All of the testing was conducted at Muroc with the tests being completed on February 18, 1944. In order to provide comparative data the YP-59A airplanes were flown in competition against a P-49D-20 and a P-38J-15. Unfortunately, for the overall P-59A program, the Y airplanes fared rather poorly against these propeller-driven machines. In performance and maneuverability the jet airplanes were outclassed by the P-47 and P-38. The one advantage that the YP-59A did have was in radius of turn and in comparison tests the XP-59A easily turned inside the P-38. However, either the P-38 or P-47 could break off combat at any time by diving away or by using full power zooms.

In evaluating the YP-59A airplanes and applying these results to the proposed production airplanes, consideration was given to all contemplated modifications planned for the P-59A-1 airplanes, but it was the decision of the Army Air Forces Board that the planned modifications to the production airplane would not significantly alter its flight characteristics or performance from the YP-59A models tested. Several rather far-reaching conclusions were made as a result of these tests, but the opinion of the Board was clearly spelled out when they stated:

"After careful analysis of all tests conducted by the Material Command Service Test Agency, the Proving

Larry Bell entering cockpit in observer seat, May 1943. (Photo courtesy of Aerophile)

Ground Command and the Army Air Forces Board, it is not believed that the P-59 airplane is operationally or tactically suited for combat nor is it believed that any modifications to this aircraft, short of a completely new design, would improve its combat suitability. . ."

In summarizing their conclusions on the overall value of the P-59A airplane, the Board stated:

"... although the aircraft is not suitable for combat, there is a requirement for a limited number of subject airplanes to be utilized for jet training and for general Air Force familiarization. The Army Air Forces Board is further of the opinion that use of jet propelled aircraft will become widespread in the immediate future and that the P-59, although unsatisfactory for tactical use, is an excellent aircraft for purposes of conducting research on jet power plants and pressure cabins. The P-59 will also make an excellent training ship in that its low wing-loading makes the airplane very safe for transition flying and the fact that it has two engines is an added safety factor."

Thus it was that, based on the performance of these YP-59A airplanes, the fate of the P-59A airplanes was sealed, for in March 1944 General Arnold stated officially that the P-59A did not appear to be the answer for an Army Air Force jet propelled fighter airplane. He further felt that the Lockheed XP-80 was more promising and that the P-59A airplanes would now be used for training purposes.

The completion of the spin program pretty well finished up the Bell test program at the desert site, and preparations were then undertaken to move the remaining effort back to the Buffalo area. The only tests not carried out at Muroc were the dive tests which, for various reasons, were scheduled to be conducted at the Niagara Falls plant at some later date. These dive tests were finally resumed at the Bell facilities in June 1944 with a YP-59A, 27-13, being used for the tests. Jack Woolams was the test pilot for this program. During the fourth dive test, on June 25, the main landing gear suddenly and quite violently extended. This accident occurred because of the high negative pressures being generated on the wing lower surfaces during the high speed dive with the result that the landing gear was literally pulled open. When this happened, the landing gear retracting links, which also served as side braces, were broken and both of the main landing gears swung freely in the breeze. Woolams did make a successful belly landing at the Niagara Falls Airport which resulted in only slight damage to the bottom of the fuselage, nacelles and wings. As a result of the accident, it was decided to provide the airplane with landing gear "up-locks" to prevent further such problems.

In order to demonstrate the dive capabilities of the airplane, the dive tests were again resumed in November 1944, but this time with a production P-59A. On each of the first four dives a structural failure of some type occurred in the horizontal stabilizer assembly. After each of these failures the damage was repaired and the structure beefed up prior to the next dive. The judgment exercised in continuing these tests in the face of the repeated structural failures is certainly open to question. However, Bell naturally desired to minimize the disparity between the actual airplane capability and its design specification, and so the dive tests continued. On the fifth dive at about 25,000 feet, luck ran out when the entire empennage was carried away, leaving Woolams trapped in the cockpit with a jammed canopy. Exhibiting that quality that makes for an outstanding test pilot, Woolams had the presence of mind to twist around in the cramped quarters of the cockpit until his back was against the seat and then he pushed the canopy loose with his feet and thus was able to safely exit from the doomed airplane. The rest was almost routine except that when his chute opened it popped so hard that he lost both his flying boots. After landing he had to run about a mile and a half in his stocking feet, in about six inches of snow, before he found an inhabited farm house. Bell was able to dispatch one of their new helicopters to him quickly enough to save his feet.

As a result of the incompletion of the demonstration dive tests, and the failures that occurred during the attempt, all of the YP-59A, P-59A-1 and P-59B-1 airplanes received a flight restriction, limiting the maximum air speed to 400 mph and speeds at various altitudes consistent with a Mach number of 0.70.

Still another problem that came out of the dive tests was that the airplane exhibited excessive longitudinal stability in the form of a positive (nose up) pitching movement at a Mach number of about 0.77. This characteristic resulted in a tendency for the airplane to pull out of a dive as the high Mach numbers were approached, thus making it quite difficult for the pilot to hold the dive attitude due to the high stick forces encountered.

The last few days at Muroc were in part used to provide passenger-carrying flights to the Bell mechanics in the open cockpit of the number one airplane. By February 18, the base was practically disbanded with the airplanes and other associated equipment being turned over to the Army Air Corps. The flight operations at the Muroc site, as far as the experimental flight testing by Bell, was officially closed on February 27, 1944, with all Bell personnel except for service and engineering departments having returned to Niagara Falls. It is certainly to Bell's credit that during their operation at Muroc, a total of three XP-59A and six YP-59A airplanes were assembled and flown for a total accumulated flying time, free of major mishaps, of 242 1/2 hours.

Just as Bell was closing out its test program, another jet program was beginning, for a few weeks earlier, the United States had acquired its second jet airplane, the Lockheed XP-80. The XP-80, nicknamed "LULA-BELLE", made its first flight at Muroc on January 8, 1944 with Lockheed's chief engineering test pilot, Milo Burcham at the controls.

As already mentioned, the YP-59A airplanes initially were almost identical to the XP-59A airplanes. However, as a result of continuing design studies and analysis of the flight tests results, several modifications were made to the Y airplanes which altered their exterior appearance. These modifications for the most part were not necessarily made at the Bell plant. The major modifications made to the YP-59A airplanes were:

1. Replacement of the original rounded wing tips with squared-off tips. This resulted in a change in wing area from 400 square feet to 386 square feet, with the wing span being reduced from 49 feet to 45 feet 6 inches.

2. A new "squared-off" vertical stabilizer and rudder were added along with the addition of a ventral fin.

3. The pitot-static tube was moved from under the left wing to the vertical stabilizer.

4. The aft fuselage was strengthened.

5. The fabric-covered flaps were replaced with metal-covered flaps.

6. Metal-covered, pressure-balanced ailerons were installed.

7. Main landing gear up-locks, mechanically operated from the cockpit, were installed.

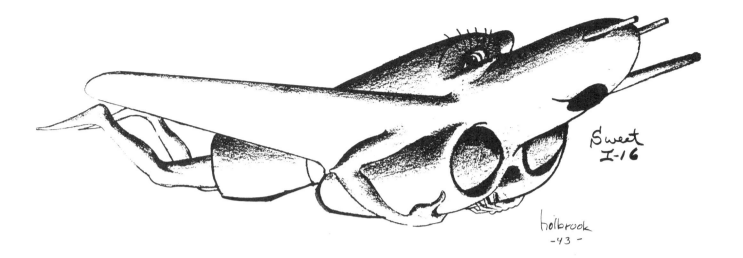

Proposed Nose Art circa 1943. (Drawing courtesy of JPA)

Over Muroc Lake #2 A/C with Bob Stanley at the controls. (Photo courtesy of GEAE)

A/C #1 XP-59A on The "Dry" Lake at Muroc. (Photo courtesy of JPA)

The GE-I-Series Engines

Type I	5 units	1250 lbs. of thrust
Type I-A1, 2	16 units	1250 lbs. of thrust
Type I-14 A, B	9 units	1400 lbs. of thrust
Type I-16A, B, C	241 units	1600 lbs. of thrust
Type I-20	Test units only	2000 lbs. of thrust

Key changes to Whittle/GE I Series of engines would be improvements in compressor/combustor design, materials/cooling, and Turbine wheel changes (fewer blades). It would not be until June of 1943 that General Electric would begin development of its own design the I-40/J33 that would go on to power the Bell XP-83 and the famous Lockheed P-80 Shooting Star.

Two of the YP-59A airplanes were used for full scale wind tunnel testing at NACA facilities. Bell 27-14 and 27-15, were tested in the NACA full scale tunnel at Langley Field, Virginia and the NACA 20-foot altitude wind tunnel at Cleveland, Ohio, respectively.

Bell had originally proposed, in late June of 1943, to build 300 P-59A airplanes. However, after considering Bell's proposal, the Army Air Force decided on the procurement of 100 of the production type airplanes. Before deciding on the procurement of the 100 airplanes, rather than 300, the Army Air Force had considered the advantages and disadvantages of the two production orders. Even though the facilities existed at the Bell factory for the production of 300 jet airplanes, such an order would result in a loss of approximately 600 P-63 airplanes. The production order for 300 planes would also have absorbed the entire I-16 production capability of General Electric, and some of the I-16 engines were required for the Navy's FR-1 airplanes. The final reasons for settling on the 100 plane order were that the quantity was sufficient for the proposed three-squadron fighter group and for additional test purposes. The formal contract with Bell was approved on March 11, 1944 with the unit cost per airplane being estimated at $123,477.00

As a result of continuing design studies to improve the range of the P-59 airplane, it was decided to install an additional 66 gallon fuel bag in each of the outer wing panels, beginning with the 21st airplane. Because this modification affected the interchangeability of the wing panels, the airplanes, beginning with the 21st, were redesignated as P-59B-1s.

On October 10, 1944, Bell received somewhat of a surprise when he was verbally notified that production on the P-59 was to be terminated with the 39th airplane. However, in reply to this, Bell felt that he should have been consulted as to the most economical point at which to stop production, and after further consideration between the Army Air Force and Bell, it was decided to cancel 50 of the P-59B-1 airplanes. The total production was then to be 20 P-59A-1s and 30 P-59B-1s with all of the P-59s having been accepted by August 27, 1945.

Apparently the first effort to preserve the number one XP-59A as a museum piece began in late February 1944, when Captain Ezra Kotcher, who was then the aircraft project engineer on the P-59, suggested such a move. The idea of retaining this rather historical aircraft was acceptable to the Army Air Force, and in late August 1944, Brig. General Carroll advised Bell that instructions were being sent for the storage of the first XP-59A at Muroc and the original flight engines at Wright Field to preserve them until their final disposition could be decided. By February 12, 1944, when the first steps to preserve the airplane were made, the number one XP-59A had accumulated a total flying time of 59 hours, 55 minutes. It is doubtful that many

more, if any, flying hours were added between February and August, and so this time is probably quite representative of the total flight time acquired during its some 23 months of service. After several months of negotiations and red tape, it was decided that the airplane would be given to the Smithsonian Institution, Washington, D.C., and on April 18, 1945, the Smithsonian officially requested the acquisition from Wright Field, where it had been sent after initially being stored at Muroc. Following arrival at the Smithsonian, it was installed in the aircraft building where it remained until it was removed for storage and repair. When first displayed at the Museum, in addition to national markings, the airplane carried the yellow serial number 2108784 on both sides of the vertical stabilizer, a large numeral "1" was painted on both sides of the fuselage nose just forward of the cockpit and the name "MISS FIRE" was lettered on the left side of the nose. Also, the second cockpit had been removed so that the airplane now resembled its original flight configuration.

The third XP-59A, 27-3, was eventually modified to have the second cockpit, and January of 1946 found this airplane still flying at Muroc. By this time, however, it had been repainted all silver and a large numeral "3" was carried on each side of the fuselage just below the open cockpit. In addition to the national markings, the airplane displayed its serial number on the vertical stabilizer. At this time the airplane was being powered by two General Electric I-16-3 engines.

Additional information concerning the fate of the other two XP-59A models, 27-2 and 27-3, is not available. However, the number two and three airplanes are officially listed as having had reclamation completed (their usable parts reclaimed) in October 1945 and April 1947, respectively.

The production allotment of the 20 P-59A airplanes was originally to be six to the Materiel Command at Wright Field with the other 14 airplanes being assigned to the 412th Fighter Group of the Fourth Air Force. Originally, the entire P-59B production of 30 planes was scheduled for delivery to the 412th. However, the requirements for the P-59A airplanes (44-22609 through 44-22628, hereafter referred to by their last three digits) was amended with only one airplane being delivered to Wright Field and the remaining 19 going to the 412th with the provision that the other five airplanes would be made available to the Materiel Command when there was a requirement for their usage. By December 1944 the delivery schedule was finalized with one P-59A being assigned to Wright Field (number 609), two to the Army Air Force Proving Ground Command, Eglin Field, Florida for use in familiarization and training of ground crews on the P-59, two to the Air Forces Board, Orlando, Florida, and the remaining 15 P-59As going to the 412th. Number 619 crashed at Dayton while being ferried to Palmdale and was washed out on November 13, 1944, 618 and 620 arrived at Bakersfield on December 9, 1944 for survey and their parts were reclaimed in January and March 1945, and 626 also underwent reclamation at Bakersfield in March 1945. In all likelihood the remaining P-59As were all delivered to the 412th and served with it from June 1945 onward.

The distinction of being the first jet airplane to travel outside of the United States, of course, goes to the YP-59A that was shipped to England. However, the first jet airplane to actually fly outside the borders of the U.S. was P-59A-1 number 610. This airplane was flown from Wright Field via the regular air transport routes to Ladd Field, Alaska, making stops at Great Falls, Montana and Edmonton, Canada and arriving on December 9, 1944. While at Ladd the airplane was attached to the Extreme Temperature Operations Unit of the Cold Weather Test Unit. It underwent 69:40 hours of flying time while stationed at Ladd without experiencing any major problems associated with the low temperature operations. The final disposition of this airplane was to the War Assets Corporation in June 1946.

Delivery of the P-59B airplanes (44-22629 through 44-22658) presented a problem because there just were not enough I-16 engines available. By the end of November 1944 Bell had sufficient engines for 26 airplanes (20 P-59As and 6 P-59Bs), and because of the Navy's priority on I-16 engines for the FR-1 program and General Electric's production distribution, it was estimated that additional engines for the P-59 program would not be available until the summer of 1945. It was therefore decided that the last of the P-59B airplanes would be accepted without engines and placed in outdoor storage by Bell until the engines became available. In late December 1944 Bell was instructed that the last 28 P-59B-1s were to be prepared for outdoor storage with each of these airplanes being flight tested and accepted prior to being placed in storage. Bell had four sets of engines in flyable condition, and the flight testing of the last airplanes was to be accomplished by the successive installation and removal of these engines until all planes had been flown.

The total of 28 planes to be stored was later reduced to 24 when it was decided that the engines would not be removed from the last four airplanes flown. However, by June 1945, this requirement was again changed, and Bell was instructed to store 16 of the planes without flight tests. The other eight were to be flight-tested and accepted, after which the engines would be removed and the airframes prepared for storage. When sufficient engines became available, Bell would install them in the planes and prepare them for flyaway. The final delivery instructions issued to Bell, in late 1945, for the P-59B airplanes were – 19 to the 412th; one (650) to NACA, Cleveland, Ohio; three (651, 657, 658) to the U.S. Navy Patuxent; one (652) to Freeman Field, Indiana; and four to Independence, Kansas for storage. This accounts for 28 airplanes, and it is possible that the other two may have been retained by Bell for tests.

The 412th Fighter Group was formed on November 30, 1943 at Muroc. From this location it moved to Palmdale, California in June 1944, to Bakersfield, California in late 1944 and to Santa Maria Army Air Field, California in July 1945. A large number of P-59 airplanes, upwards of 25 or more, were stationed at this field, but by late June of 1945 all of the P-59 airplanes had been assigned to Base Operations or one of the Squadrons (Training) of the 440th Army Air Force Base Unit. As of September 1945 the 412th Fighter Group consisted of the 29th Fighter Squadron, 31st Fighter Squadron, 445th Fighter Squadron, 361st Fighter Squadron, 615th Air Engineering Squadron and the 624th Air Materiel Squadron. In October 1945 the 361st Fighter Squadron became a Service Group for the 412th Fighter Group with the 615th Air Engineering Squadron and the 624th Air Materiel Squadron being assigned to the newly-formed 361st Service Group. In December 1945 the 412th Fighter Group was transferred to March Field, Riverside, California. After the transfer to March Field the 412th was equipped with P-80s. The Group, in 1966, consisted of the 71st Fighter Squadron (445th FS), 94th Fighter Squadron (29th FS) 27th Fighter Squadron (31st FS), 39th TAC Recon Squadron and the 361st Service Group.

In addition to the A and B models stationed at Santa Maria, there was also one YP-59A stationed there, and it had been modified to have a second cockpit. This airplane was sometimes used to take ground personnel and nurses (there was a field hospital at Santa Maria) for their first jet flight. This airplane was 27-16, 42-108777, and in June 1946 it was given to a school in Northern California, Cal Poly, and from here it was later acquired by Ed Maloney for display at the Air Museum, Ontario, California. Quite a bit of flying was done with the P-59s at Santa Maria, and in relating some of his experiences with the P-59, Mr. C.B. Coenen, had the following story to tell concerning a wheels-up landing:

"One pilot, name unknown, made a good initial takeoff, but in landing he neglected to put down his landing gear. Despite repeated exhortations over the R/T, he came in wheels up and skidded on the engine nacelles for about 50-100 feet before he realized his error. He gave it power, took off and came around and made a normal wheels-down landing. The engines had to be changed and major repair performed on the nacelles and frame to put it back in flying condition."

In January 1946 the inactivation of Santa Maria was undertaken, and at this time many of the P-59s were flown to March Field for use by the 412th. The remaining P-59s were ferried directly from Santa Maria to other locations in the United States, with several of them going to Land Grant Colleges. All of the P-59s delivered to March Field were shortly disposed of, by July 1946 there were no more P-59 airplanes at March Field. The P-59s given to colleges were used for instructional

Roy Shoults (seated) checks spring scale that measures installed thrust of I-A in XP-59A as Bell's Bob Stanley (standing left) checks progress. (Assumption was that the scale was in the rear of the plane attached to a solid object and tied to the rear wheels, otherwise why would one pull the aircraft if the scale was attached to the front wheel - unless. . . and so it goes!!) Also, behind Roy Shoults is Don Bulton, in the foreground is Ed Rhoades with Arthur Fornoff to the right and behind R. Stanley is H. Poyer. (Photo courtesy of GEAE)

Excellent view of the three .50 cal. machine guns - left and single 37mm cannon.(Photo courtesy of JPA)

A/C No. #2 over Muroc "Dry" Lake 1942 later to become Edwards Air Force Base.(Photo courtesy of JPA)

Gus Berg of GE viewing right engine inlet and engine arrangement.(Photo courtesy of JPA)

purposes and then junked. One exception was P-59B-1, 44-22656, which was originally given to Purdue University. This airplane was sold by Purdue in 1956 to the Harold Warp Pioneer Village, Minden, Nebraska.

From March through July 1946, 17 P-59s (three P-59As including 617 and 623, and 14 P-59Bs – 629, 634, 635, 636, 637, 639 thru 645, 648 and 654) were assigned and delivered to the U.S. Army Aberdeen Proving Ground, Maryland. These airplanes were used for static aircraft vulnerability experiments and then salvaged. The planes were apparently scrapped by 1949. The last P-59 on the Air Force inventory was 44-22633 which was salvaged at Muroc as a ZF-59B on October 4, 1948.

The three P-59Bs that went to the Navy had relatively longer lives. Number 651 became BuNo 64100, coming into Navy service on October 17, 1945 and last being Number 657, BuNo 64109, was delivered on February 12, 1946 and scrapped at Norfolk on December 22, 1947. Both of these planes were first used for jet familiarization at NATC, Patuxent River, Maryland. Number 658, BuNo 64108, was delivered on January 15, 1946 and used by Tactical Test at NATC, Patuxent River. It crashed on December 8, 1947 with 142 total airframe hours and was subsequently barged to Norfolk for scrapping on April 16, 1948.

Another P-59 that survived the years is P-59B-1, 44-22650. After being at NACA, Cleveland, it arrived at Kirtland Air Force Base, New Mexico in 1947. The airplane was to be used as a target in the development of proximity fuses for artillery shells at a test site located along the foot of the Manzano Mountains, just east of Kirtland. Although many airplanes were destroyed during this program, the P-59B somehow was spared from being used as a target, and during the period from 1947 to 1951 it remained at a little dirt airstrip in Coyote Canyon, Manzano Mountains.

In 1951, the P-59 and a Japanese Oscar were placed as a war memorial in front of Kirtland's base headquarters building. However, the maintenance of the airplanes proved to be costly, and in about 1953 a new base CO decided that the airplanes were an eyesore and so the two planes were moved to the Base Reclamation Area where they were to be destroyed. Fortunately, R.F. Arnold, Base Supply Officer with the New Mexico Air National Guard recognized the historical significance of these airplanes, and he arranged to have them transferred to the Air National Guard Supply account. For the next couple of years they shared the flight line on the west side of Kirtland with Air National Guard F-80s.

Then in 1955 someone from the Air Force Museum noticed the P-59, and shortly thereafter the New Mexico Air National Guard received a request to donate the airplane to the Museum. Thus, on December 23, 1955 the P-59 was presented to the Air Force Museum in ceremonies conducted at Kirtland. Brig. General John P. McFarland, then New Mexico's assistant adjutant general for air, Air National Guard, presented the

airplane to Brig. General W.M. Canterbury, then Commander of the Air Force Special Weapons Center, Kirtland. General Canterbury then took the necessary steps required to have the airplane forwarded to the Air Force Museum.

The news that the United States was active in the jet propulsion field and, in fact, had flown a jet-powered airplane was not made public until late in the afternoon of January 6, 1944, when this information was released from the Army Air Force pressroom at the Pentagon. Being typical of wartime news releases, this joint Army Air Forces-Royal Air Force announcement was rather vague and offered very few details of the airplane. Basically, it gave a brief history of jet propulsion, which included such information as the fact that Group Captain Frank Whittle had designed and developed the jet engine and that the Gloster airplane had first flown in May 1941. The release went on to say that the Bell experimental airplane, powered by General Electric engines that were based on the Whittle engine, first flew on October 1, 1942 with Robert M. Stanley as pilot and that on the next day Col. Laurence C. Craigie flew the airplane to become the first Army officer to fly a jet. The release failed to mention the location where the first flight occurred, the name of the airplane, or its designation.

No photographs were included, and it was September 1944 before the first ones were released to the press. The lack of fanfare and publicity on the XP-59A is certainly a far cry from today's gala and well-reported roll-outs and first flights of a new design. Of course, when the XP-59A was making its place in history, the wartime secrecy of the project prevented the airplane and the people associated with it from receiving the credit they so justly deserved. Unfortunately, by the time that details of the P-59 could be revealed, the airplane had already been delegated to a training role with the Lockheed P-80 having come into the limelight.

Commenting on the new "rocket ship", as the newspapers called it, Larry Bell on January 7, 1944 issued the following statement:

> "We believe that the hundreds of successful flights made by Bell jet-propelled ships opens a new chapter in American aviation history.
>
> "Bell Aircraft has built the first American fighter planes powered by jet propulsion engines constructed by the General Electric Company from British designs.
>
> "They prove a new scientific principle – that planes can fly without propellers. Once a principle is proved, count on engineering genius of the Allied Powers to develop it into greater performance records, not only to help speed the day of victory but to pave the way towards new achievements in a postwar aviation world."

The release of the news disclosing the existence of a jet plane naturally touched off wide-spread speculation on the performance of this new and revolutionary

airplane. Typical of the comments appearing in the trade magazines were, "Speed of the plane was placed at between 500 and 600 mph." and "Its top speed has been estimated by ground observers to exceed 500 mph." The writers of these remarks were obviously influenced by rather optimistic enthusiasm because the maximum speeds for the XP-59A were about 350 mph at sea level to 390 mph at 30,000 feet. In fact, the official performance tests carried out on the YP-59A equipped with the more powerful I-16 engines only provided a maximum speed of 409 mph at 35,000 and about the highest speed ever quoted for any of the P-59 models was 425 mph.

Obviously the P-59 was not a success in the role for which it was originally designed, however, in another respect it was an unqualified success for the people of the Army Air Force, Bell and General Electric. Starting from scratch and several years behind the British and Germans, this team designed, produced and flew a jet-powered airplane that was to provide the United States with much-needed experience during a critical and trying period in its history.

The final report covering the development of the X and Y airplanes was issued on June 28, 1945, and the closing paragraph of this document provides an adequate summary of the program:

> "Even though a combat airplane did not result from the development of the X and YP-59A airplanes, it is considered that the development was very worthwhile, since it proved that the principle of jet propulsion for aircraft was sound and practical, and the airplanes themselves will be good training airplanes for pilots who will fly later jet propelled airplanes into combat."

Key /B=Bell, /GE=General Electric, /USAAC=United States Army Air Corps.
(Photo courtesy of J. Brown)

Full GE, Bell and U.S. Army Air Corps crew after the first official flight October 2, 1942. Top row l-r, Robert Stanley/B, Herbert Bowers/B, Robert Schroeder/B, Joseph Brown/B, Robert Wolf/B, Edgar Rhodes/B. Middle row l-r, UK, Larry Bell/B, Jim George/B, Harlan Poyer/B, Roy Schoults/GE, Marty Valetich/B, Jack Russell/B, Ed Tritle/GE, Col. Craigie/USAAC, Russell Single/B, George Gorgan/B, Arthur Fornoff/B. Front rown l-r, Angus McEachern/GE, UK, Melvin Kensinger/B, Lee Parker/ B, Willian Winegar/B, Al Kowalski/B, James Limage/B, Edward Murphy/B, Ted Rogers/GE, Frank Burnham/GE, UK, Capt. Joe Dodd/USAAC.

Bell's Ill-Fated Second Airplane Design, The First XP-59B

as told by R. Wolf, a member of Bell's "Secret Six" Design Team.

I would like to tell you a bit about Bell Aircraft's second jet airplane design, a story known only to a few people and not found in the usual annals of aviation history. It could well be the second best-kept secret in the early years of the jet airplane development in America.

Some of us, who had designed the XP-59A knew "in our bones" that although it was a glorious achievement — the airplane would, even if modified with smaller wings and more fuel would be only marginally competitive with the up-coming generation of propeller driven fighters by the time we could get it into combat.

The 1600 pounds of thrust of the I-16 engine would not be enough to beat the new propeller airplanes on the drawing boards which were planning to use the new

powerful piston engines, such as the Pratt & Whitney R-2800 which was to put out 2000 horsepower, and the R-4360 aiming at 4000 H.P. as planned for the original Bell XP-59 airplane.

So, during the winter of 1942 and spring of 1943, after the early flight testing of the XP-59A our engineering group at Main St. in Buffalo which was still intact — began design of a single-engined jet fighter under the prompting of Col. Don Keirn of the U.S. Army Air Force. He believed that a British de Havilland H-1 (Goblin) engine could be made available to us as a starting point, and that it — and as other British engines materialized with greater thrust, could be fitted into the same airplane, to create a really superior, high-performance single engined fighter for the U.S. The de

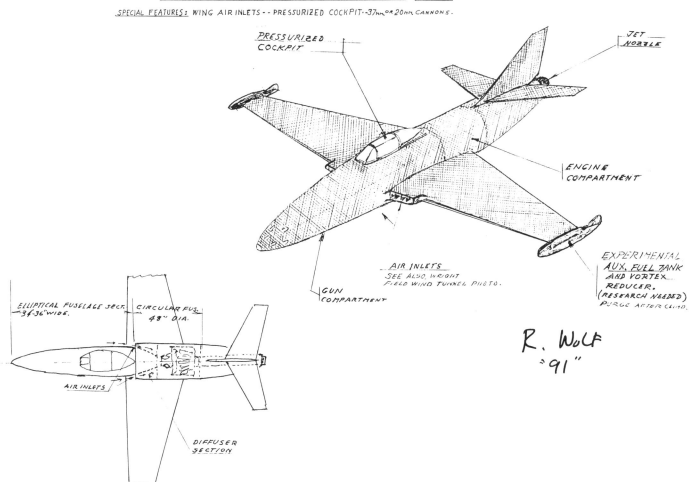

PRELIMINARY DESIGN ~ BELL XP59-B
SINGLE ENGINE JET FIGHTER ~ 42-43
SPECIAL FEATURES: WING AIR INLETS -- PRESSURIZED COCKPIT - 37mm or 20mm CANNONS.

PRESSURIZED COCKPIT

JET NOZZLE

ENGINE COMPARTMENT

AIR INLETS
SEE ALSO, WRIGHT FIELD WIND TUNNEL PHOTO.

GUN COMPARTMENT

EXPERIMENTAL AUX. FUEL TANK AND VORTEX REDUCER.
(RESEARCH NEEDED)
PURGE AFTER CLIMB

R. WOLF "91"

ELLIPTICAL FUSELAGE SECT. 36-36" WIDE.

CIRCULAR FUS. 48" DIA.

AIR INLETS

DIFFUSER SECTION

Single engine Bell model. XP-59"B" wind tunnel model at Wright field for air inlet refinements. (Photo courtesy of R. Wolf)

Havilland Goblin H-1 engine, designed under Maj. Frank Halford's direction, had promise of reaching 2000 lbs of thrust by early 1943 (which it did) and then, with further development it hit 3000 pounds, and finally put out 3500 pounds of thrust by the time we would have reached initial flight testing of the XP-59-B experimental airplane with its earlier engine.

The Rolls-Royce W.2B-37 series had also come a long way since Whittle's first design and now called the Derwent was also a possible candidate for our new airplane. The Derwent series would reach 3000 pounds output and became the principal engine for the British Meteor as it went into service.

So, we went to work on the preliminary design of "the next Bell jet" with great enthusiasm. Here was the real thing! A real fighter!

Knowledge of these advanced British engine designs also stimulated Col. Keirn to urge General Electric to start development of a 3000 to 4000 pound engine of the centrifugal type, a most noteworthy goal which would provide a competitive American source. This engine became the G.E. I-40, which by mid-1944 had reached 3750 pounds of thrust on the test stand. It finally went on to be rated at 4000 pounds of thrust and was designated as the J33.

We, at Bell, labeled our new design the XP-59B, not to be confused with the modified version of the XP-59A which eventually was called the XP-59, or P-59 in A and B series as it became a jet trainer. Using the same contractual means to maintain secrecy (adding a new letter, B) to the original XP-59. We were aiming for a 600 mph airplane.

By June of 1943 we had decided on a low wing configuration with the engine "buried" in the fuselage behind the pilot and with air inlets in the wing leading edge. I designed these inlets with a turning interior diffuser aided by testing at low velocity in a smoke tunnel operated by Roger Griswald, and then refined in the larger wind tunnel at Wright Field.

We had good drawings of the H-1 Goblin engine and were starting preliminary design of the airplane, keeping in mind and making space provisions for other engines to follow.

Then in July of 1943 I went to England with Col. Keirn on a mission to review the very active and extensive British research and development program on this second generation of jet engines. A program not only to create a new fighter to defend England in WWII, but also aimed at future "Capture" of world commercial jets of the post war era. I was amazed at the creativity and scope of the program and was anxious to get back home to work on the XP-59B and plan for its future with more powerful engines. America had nothing like this in process. The British lead in jet engine development was most impressive. It was also obvious to me, but not yet fully accepted by centrifugal compressor enthusiasts, that a trend toward axial flow types of engines would probably dominate the future.

So, you can imagine my surprise — and bitter disappointment to learn when we returned to the States, full of great expectations and ideas, to find that our Bell XP-59B airplane design had been cancelled and the information, drawings and British engine were being turned over to the Lockheed Aircraft Co. with a contract to design and build a single-engined jet fighter, with the same objectives that we had established for the XP-59B.

I shall never know the real reasons for this abrupt turnabout of the Army Air Force, in transferring our project to Lockheed. It may have had something to do with Bell's already having too much on its hands, what with the fighter plant at Niagara Falls and the B-29 Bomber plant at Atlanta. I should like to have known what went on in those conversations between Larry Bell, Gen. Chidlaw, and perhaps Gen. Arnold.

Whatever the reason — it was the death knell for Bell's survival in the jet airplane field. Being first, of itself, does not always pay off!

The glory of the Bell XP-59A adventure was that we were the First . . . but the great disappointment, especially to me . . . was that Bell Aircraft dropped out of the race by not pursuing the XP-59B.

Big Brother

The Airacomet also had a Big Brother. Bell Model 49 (XP-83) powered by two GE I-40 (J33) engines producing 3750 lbs of thrust each. In March of 1943, it was considered as an interceptor but was redesigned in April as a long-range escort fighter. On March 24, 1944 contract W33-038-AC was awarded for two prototypes, wind tunnel models and engineering design needs. Actually, an enlarged Airacomet with a sliding bubble canopy and large internal fuel cells of 1031 gallons total, it was abandoned after only two prototypes were built. This Big Brother was able to reach a top speed of 522 mph at 15,660 ft, while its cruising speed was 441 mph. Its empty weight was 16,022 lbs, its gross 21,723 lbs, with a maximum mammoth 27,500 lbs. It possessed six .50 caliber guns with 1800 rounds when flown on February 27, 1945. The second prototype flew on October 19 with six .60 caliber TITE3 Browning high cyclic rate of fire guns. It carried a wing span of 35 ft, a length of 44 ft 10" and a height of 15' 3". The total wing area was 431 square feet with a wing loading of 39.67 pounds per square foot compared to the P-59A with its light 25 lbs/sq ft. wing load.

Bell was notified by NACA in September of 1944 that wind tunnel test showed the XP-83 to be directionally unstable. An additional 18" was added to the vertical fin and rudder on the second aircraft (44-84991) but with the wars' end in sight the aircraft was sent to Wright Field for gun testing and dropped out of sight. The first prototype was assigned to Bell for Ram Jet testing and the program came to a quick end when the Ram Jet caught fire and set the wing afire. The test pilot and engineer bailed out and (44-84990) crashed in a nearby field. This ended Bell's fixed wing aircraft history.

XP-83 - Bell model 49 at Bell factory circa 1944 - only two made. (Photo courtesy of J. Brown)

XP-83 Bell's big "Airacomet" with I-40/J33 4000 lb. thrust GE engines - too big - too late and unstable. (Photo courtesy of J. Brown)

XP-83 with Ram jet that would cause a wing fire and put an end to Bell's fixed wing jet aircraft history. (Photo courtesy of JPA)

Post Script

It is important to note that while the Whittle/GE I-A series of engines were in production, both GE and some British companies were hard at work (1942 - 43) designing a 3000/4000 lb thrust engine for the War effort. The British, through Major Frank Halford, designed a "straight-through" unit instead of the classic reverse flow type that Whittle had designed. Another Halford difference was its utilization of a single sided impeller which gives high velocity to the incoming combustor air much like the then current supercharger impeller designs. On the other hand, GE remained with the double sided impeller but did so with the "straight through" design, producing the I-40 or J33 that would go on to power the Lockheed P-80 "Shooting Star". It had always been clear that a straight through design would be more efficient, but longer in length, with an added problem of rotor dynamic balance due to the increased distance between the impeller and turbine wheel.

Concurrent with the above, GE had been hard at work on an axial flow compressor engine (TG-100) in Schenectady since late 1941 which was more like the German Junker's Jumo 004. Due to reasons concerning compressor efficiency and smaller frontal area, this design was to become the standard for all future engines of larger thrust. However the centrifugal would come back in such engines as the 1500 shp GE12 of the late 1960's which used five axial stages up front and a final centrifugal impeller stage, and would go on to become the GE- T700.

R. Standerwick with the GE - I-40/J33 that powered the XP-83 and XP-80. Below is GE's first axial flow turbojet engine the TG180. The TG - 100 before it was the world's second turboprop engine. (Photo courtesy of GEAE)

GE TG180/J35

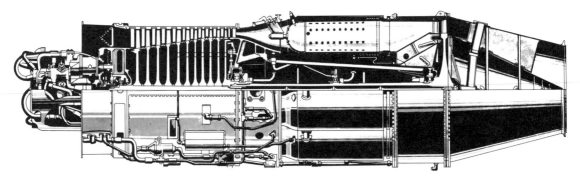

German Jumo 004 used in the Me 262

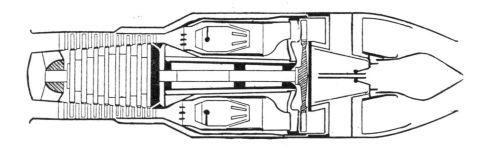

She Flies Again

The
Air
Museum

"Planes of Fame" P-59A project workers (left to right, back row) John Maloney, Jim Cass, Bob Reed, (left to right, front row) Matt Mauch and Kyle Rohman with the Bell YP-59A Airacomet that the Air Museum is restoring to flying condition at the Chino Airport in southern California. The Air Museum's "Airacomet" is being restored in the 50th anniversary year of its first flight which took place on October 2, 1941.

P-59 Workteam At Textron Aerostructures

Textron Aerostructures, Nashville, Tennessee received the forward fuselage and wings in 1991. Some evaluation was done on the fuselage section and was shipped back to Chino, California. Textron is machining parts for the fuselage. The wings remained at Textron for refurbishment. The repairs are extensive due to corrosion on both wings on the upper and lower rear spar caps. These will be machined and replaced by volunteer workers on their own time at Textron. Some internal rib structures will have to be duplicated and replaced along with the majority of the wing skin panels. Trailing edge and leading edge skin panels will also be formed and replaced. All landing gear parts will be pulled out and sent to another source to be refurbished.

P-59 Workteam at Textron Aerostructures. Front row: (l-r) Gary N. Brooks, Dorris G. Davenport, James Plunkett, R.G. Sluder, Chester Myers. Middle row: (l-r) Billy Kemp, David Pursley, Dennis Ingram, William Stafford, Frank Witscheber. Back row: (l-r) Walter Taylor, James Webb, Michael Vetetoe, Brad Dexter.

Front 1st: GE-Bob Bell, B. Mangan, J. Benjamin. Chino Air Museum-J. Benjamin. MRC BRGS- S. Allen. Ryder Aviall- C. Hill, T. Deitrick, L. Dyke. 2nd: J. Hernandez, B. Onyshko, B. Watkins, V. Checkcino,F. Bentley, G. Melikian. 3rd: G. Gonzales, W. Chmielewski, T. Duggan, D. Bogacz, Z. Sevoian, T. Pitts, D. Del Paine.

Pictured above is the majority of the Ryder Aviall Burbank team that overhauled three General Electric I-16 engines from the 1940's for the use in the YP-59A owned by the "Planes of Fame" Air Museum in Chino, California. Ryder Aviall, a subsidiary of Ryder System Inc., is an independent turbine engine overhaul company in the US. The Burbank facility that overhauled the I-16s is part of the larger group based in Dallas, Texas.

In August of 1991, John Benjamin, representing the "Planes of Fame" Air Museum contacted Carl Hill, of the Burbank operations, and asked if Ryder Aviall would be willing to restore three I-16 engines for use in the Army YP-59A airplane that the museum was planning to make fly again. A great love for airplanes caused Hill to agree to accept the challenge as did dozens of other Burbank employees. Hundreds of hours were donated by those employees and thousands of dollars were spent before the three engines were completed.

The engines were Navy engines used in the FR-1, Ryan Fireball, but the same type as used in the original YP-59A. They had been in unprotected storage since 1946 in New Mexico and were eventually obtained by the museum and finally sent to Ryder Aviall for overhaul. Getting them ready for use in the Army YP-59A pre-

sented many problems. The Navy had removed the generators and the gears that drove them from the gearbox. The diffuser case had to be reindexed as the Navy mounted the engine differently. This in turn meant that the ball mount support had to be modified for a different angle. The accessories proved to be of a different configuration especially the fuel system components and plumbing. The ignition system and thermocouple systems having been mounted in the airplane were non-existent. These were only a few of the problems to be overcome, not to mention the fact that replacement parts were usually no longer made.

Terry Deitrick spearheaded the effort of Aviall and the several other companies that were brought into the overhaul effort. The MRC Bearing Company supplied all new bearings of the latest state of the art material. GE Aircraft Engines of Lynn Massachusetts and the Jet Pioneers of America supplied documents, parts, manuals and technical assistance whenever needed and the U.S. Armys' Corpus Christi Overhaul Depot in Texas repaired the gear boxes. With expertise, ingenuity, a lot of "engineering resourcefulness" the Overhaul Team rose to the challenges, overcame the problems and produced three fully restored I-16 engines.

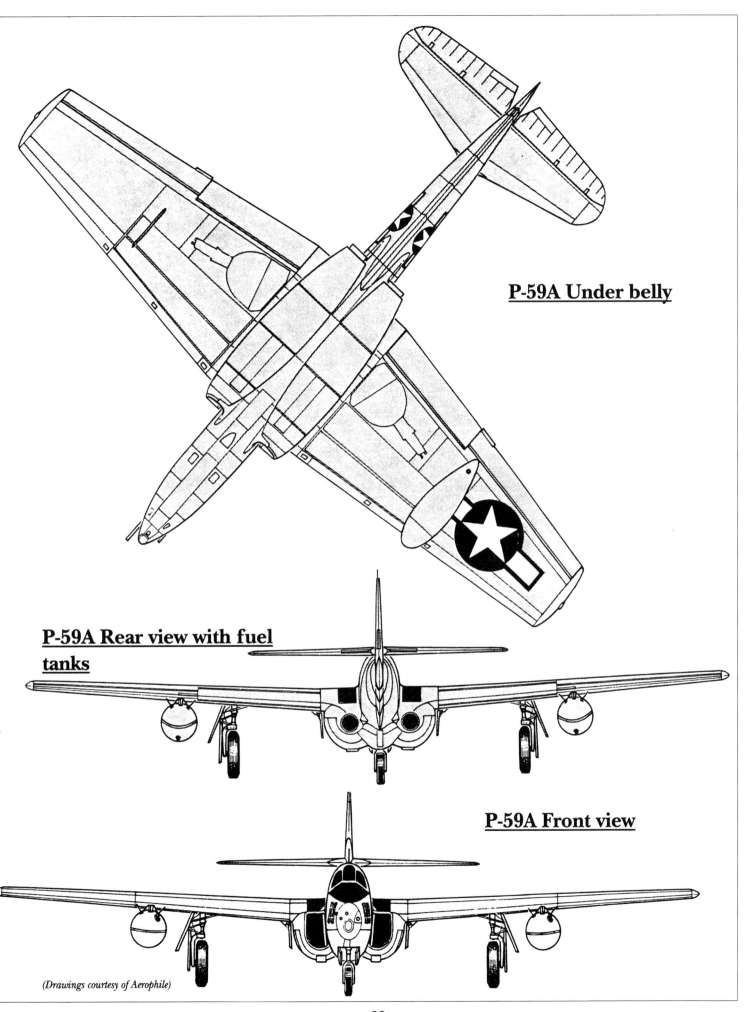

P-59A Under belly

P-59A Rear view with fuel tanks

P-59A Front view

(Drawings courtesy of Aerophile)

PHYSICAL CHARACTERISTICS XP-59A

Airplane - General:

Overall Span	49'0"
Overall Length, Cannon Tip	38'10"
Overall Height, Thrust Line Level	14'6"
Overall Height, At Rest	12'3 3/4"
Clearance, Bottom of Nacelle, Thrust Line Level	2'0"
Clearance, Bottom of Nacelle, At Rest	1'5 3/4"

Wings:

Airfoil Section N.A.C.A. Root	66, 2•014
Tip	66, 2x•212
Total Area, Including Ailerons and Flaps	400 sq. ft.
Root Chord (45 in. Outboard of Centerline of Airplane Splice)	10'8"
Tip Chord (266 1/2 in. Outboard of Centerline of Airplane)	5'0"
Incidence, Root	+2°
Tip	0°
Dihedral, 45% Line	3°30'
Sweepback	7°

Ailerons:

Area, Aft of Hinge Centerline 12.0 sq. ft.	
Area, Balance	3.5 sq. ft.
Area, Total (Each)	15.5 sq. ft.
Movement	Up 25°
	Down 10°
Area (Each Tab)	1.14 sq. ft.
Movement (Tab)	Up 25°
	Down 10°
Area (Each Tab)	1.14 sq. ft.
Movement (Tab)	Up 10°
	Down 10°

Flaps:

Area, Aft of Hinge Centerline	12.95 sq. ft.
Area, Balance	3.68 sq. ft.
Area, Total (Each)	16.63 sq. ft.
Span (Total)	15' 7 3/4"
Movement	Down 45°

Empennage:

(1) Horizontal Stabilizer:

Area (Stabilizer)	45.63 sq. ft.
Area (Horizontal Tail)	69.86 sq. ft.
Incidence (Fixed)	1 1/4°
Chord (Root, Including Elevator)	72"
Span	16' 8"

(2) Elevator:

Area, Aft of Hinge Centerline	10.06 sq. ft.
Area, Balance	2.05 sq. ft.
Area, Total (Each)	12.11 sq. ft.
Movement	Up 25°
	Down 15°
Area, (Each Tab)	.83 sq. ft.
Movement	Up 15°
	Down 15°

(2) Vertical Stabilizer:

Area, (Fin)	17.75 sq. ft.
Area, (Vertical Tail)	32.35 sq. ft.
Chord (Root, Including Rudder)	88"
Span	7' 5"

(4) Rudder:

Area, Aft of Hinge Centerline	12.60 sq. ft.
Area, Balance	2.0 sq. ft.
Area, Total (Each)	14.60 sq. ft.
Movement	Right 25°
	Left 25°
Area, (Each Tab)	.63 sq. ft.
Movement	Right 15°
	Left 15°

Landing Gear:

Tread	222"
Main Wheel Axle Centerline Aft of Leading Edge of Wing	61.5"

P-59 SERIAL NUMBERS

Model	AAF S/N	No. Produced
XP-59A	42-108784 / 42-108786	3
YP-59A	42-108771 / 42-108783	13
P-59A-1		20
P-59B-1		30

SECTION I
INTRODUCTION

1. This publication comprises the service instructions for the Types I-16B5 and I-16B7 aircraft gas turbines for jet propulsion and the associated model Type I-16B4, manufactured by the General Electric Company, Schenectady, New York. The Types I-16B5 and I-16B7 have been taken as the standard in compiling this handbook. Differences between these and other Type I models will be found in Appendix I of the Handbook of Overhaul Instructions, CO-AN 02-105-3.

2. Jet propulsion can best be illustrated by the use of a toy balloon, as shown in figure 5.

3. The Type I-16 is a new unit and radically different power plant for dynamic aircraft. It is a distinct departure from the conventional aviation engine in that it is constructed on different engineering principles; it has a different means of propulsion; and its operation and performance are correspondingly different. Its power, altitude, and speed are outstanding, since it operates without propellers. It produces more power for its weight than any aviation engine known to exist. Aircraft powered with it have reached higher altitudes carrying a combat load greater than any other military aircraft, yet the gas turbine requires no accessory superchargers. And it has sustained speeds hitherto unknown to aeronautics. In addition, it has an almost instantaneous take-off, requiring only a fraction of a minute to warm up. Having no propeller and only a single major moving part, it is practically without vibration, and makes far less noise; in fact, its approach is virtually soundless. It is light in weight, less complex in construction, simple to operate, and inexpensive to maintain.

4. Furthermore, it is a complete aircraft power plant. being complete in itself, it does not need such power-plant accessories as oil coolers, additional superchargers, intercoolers, air ducts, or the controls necessary for the operation of such devices. It is mounted by three points of suspension, figure 6, in a specially designed air compartment in the fuselage or nacelle of the airplane. The space around the power plant is so constructed as to form a plenum chamber about the compressor, enabling the

unit to be abundantly supplied with air. In flight, this region is rammed by efficiently diffused air drawn in through an aperture at the front. Connected to the exhaust cone at the rear of the unit is a tail pipe which provides a passage of escape for the exhaust gas. The only other exterior connections are for electricity, fuel, lubrication, and five power-plant instruments.

5. Operation of the I-16 unit is relatively simple compared with that of conventional airplane power plants of high rating. All that is required of the pilot for starting is to throw an electric switch, push a starter button, and operate the throttle valve. In less than a minute, the airplane is ready for take-off. The number of power-plant instruments needed is small compared to that required for the operation of other aviation power plants. At the present time, there are only five power-plant instruments, figure 7, to be observed; these record exhaust temperature, burner pressure, lubricating-oil pressure, bearing temperature, and rotor speed. This simplicity of operation relieves the pilot of all attention to the power plant, and gives him full opportunity to tend to his business of combat and flight.

6. This unit is particularly adaptable to high-altitude flight, inasmuch as it is both an aircraft gas turbine and a turbosupercharger in a single unit, with all the speed and altitude which the alliance of these two power-producing agents makes possible. The conventional airplane engine loses its efficiency as it climbs to altitude because of the gradual decrease in the density of the air to both the engine and the propeller. Hence, in order to restore to the engine air density approximating that of sea level, it must be equipped with a supercharger or turbosupercharger to compress the rarefied air of the atmosphere for efficient operation. The propeller, however, still has to cope with the rarefied air. The I-16 unit, on the other hand, climbs to altitude under its own power without requiring any additional power-increasing devices. It has no propeller problem. And, since air resistance is greatly reduced at high altitudes, the greater speed and efficiency of high-altitude flying are made possible.

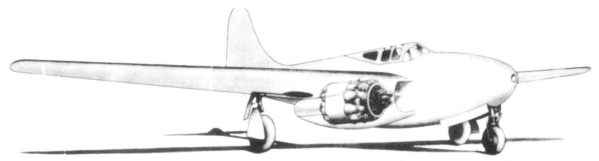

Figure 6—Diagrammatic Installation of Aircraft Gas Turbine for Jet Propulsion

SECTION III
TABLE OF SPECIFICATIONS

Model I-16
Type .... Aircraft Internal-combustion Gas Turbine for Jet Propulsion.
Number of Combustion Chambers 10

GENERAL

Exhaust Pipe (Attached to engine exhaust cone)
    Length .... 55 in.
    Diameter .... 14 1/4 in.
Jet Nozzle (attached to tail pipe)
    Length .... 9 1/2 in.
    Area(at nozzle exit) .... 120.86/119.74 sq. in.
Normal Rating (sea level)
    Thrust .... 1425 lb.
    Speed .... 16,000 rpm
    Exhaust temperature .... 115°F (621.1° C)
Military Rating (sea level)
    Thrust .... 1610 lb
    Speed .... 16,500 rpm
    Exhaust temperature .... 1220°F (660.0°C)
Five-minute Rating
    Thrust ⎱ corresponding to exhaust-gas temperature
    Speed ⎰
    Exhaust temperature not to
      exceed .... 1240° F (671.1° C)
Altitude .... 50,000 ft
Idling Speed (sea level) .... 5000 rpm
Weights
    Aircraft gas turbine without accessories .... 804 lb.
    Aircraft gas turbine with attached accessories
                                     885.2 lb.
    Unattached accessories .... 21.18 lb.
Mounting .... 2 Trunnions
                            1 Ball Support
Dimensions
    Diameter .... 41 1/2 in.
    Length .... 72 in.
    Width .... 41 in.
    Height Over Fittings .... 44 in.

IGNITION

Spark Plug
    No. .... 2 (Combustion chambers Nos. 4 and 8)
    Type .... 7HS16A1 (G. E. Co.)
    Gap .... 0.070 in. min.—0.080 in. max.
Coil .... 57G710-1 (G. E. Co.)

FUEL SYSTEM

Fuel .... Kerosene
    Specification VV-K-211a
    Grade X
    Fuel Pump, Main .... 1-P-587-B (Pesco)
    Fuel Pump, Starting ...... 1-A (Type 1297), Eclipse)

LUBRICATION SYSTEM

Oil Specification 3580D
Oil Pump .... C14C14C28B (Nichols)
Oil Tank .... 2 Gal

INSTRUMENT CONNECTIONS

Temperature   Pressures
    Exhaust gases of tail pipe ...... Lubricating-oil pressure
    Rotor rear bearing .... Burner-manifold fuel pressure
Speed
    Tachometer for power-plant rotor speed

ACCESSORIES

ATTACHED ACCESSORIES	Model No.	Mfr.	Weight, Lb.
Generator	2CM61B3	G. E. Co.	23.5
Starter	2CM42B3	G. E. Co.	21.0
Pump - Main Fuel	1-P-587-B	Pesco	9.9
Pump - Starting Fuel	1-A (Type 1297)	Eclipse	3.8
Pump - Lube and Scavenger	C14C14C28B	Nichols	4.9
Governor	7HGL16A1	G. E. Co.	7.9
Tachometer Generator	2CM5-ACF	G. E. Co.	2.9
Valve - Drip and Meter	7HVDM16A1	G. E. Co.	1.5
Valve - Combustion-Chamber Drain	7HVC16A1	G. E. Co.	.6
Spark Plugs	7HS16A1	G. E. Co.	.6
Valve - Check and Relief	7HVR16A1	G. E. Co.	.9
Filter - Lube Oil	G-159J-21	Purolator	1.5
Valve - Lube Oil Relief	7HVL16A1	G. E. Co.	.6
Filter-Air	PA-12	Purolator	1.6

UNATTACHED ACCESSORIES	Model No.	Mfr.	Weight, Lb.
Barometric	7HVB16A1	G. E. Co.	4.5
Valve - Throttle	7HVT16A1	G. E. Co.	1.95
Stopcock	7HVS16A1	G. E. Co.	1.94
Relay	3GTR72C8	G. E. Co.	2.13
Coil-Ignition	57G710-1	G. E. Co.	.875
Filter - Fuel	AAS-3/4-10	Fulflo	1.41
Tank - Oil	7HT16A1	G. E. Co.	7.5
Tail Pipe		Furnished by Airplane Mfr.	
Tail-pipe Nozzle		Furnished by Airplane Mfr.	

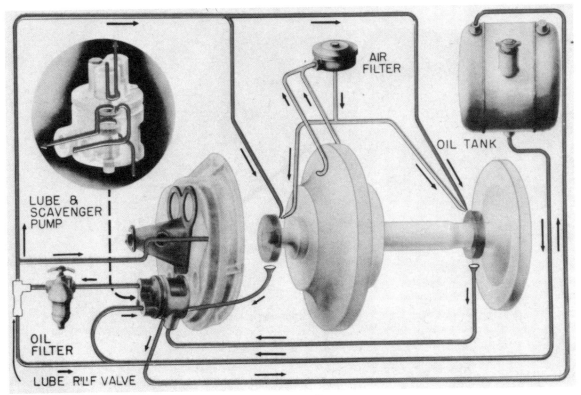

OIL   AIR
Figure 19—Lubrication System

Figure 12—Centrifugal Air Compressor

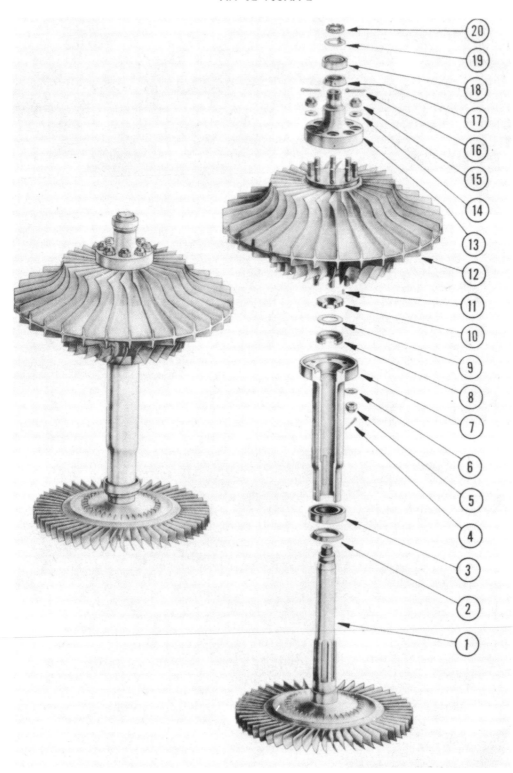

1 Turbine wheel and shaft, "0" etched on threaded end of shaft
2 Rear oil slinger, "0" etched on slanting face
3 Turbine ball bearing, "Z" stamped on inner race
4 Cotter pin
5 Castellated nut
6 Washer
7 Rear shaft, "0" etched on flange
8 Spring collar, "0" etched on narrow face
9 Shims
10 Shaft lock nut
11 Locking dowel
12 Impeller, "0" stamped on stud or etched on flange
13 Front shaft, "0" etched on flange
14 Washer
15 Castellated nut
16 Cotter pin
17 Front oil slinger, "0" etched on slanting face
18 Compressor ball bearing, "U" stamped on inner race
19 Tab lock washer
20 Front-shaft lock nut

Figure 13—Rotor Assembly

RESTRICTED

Figuure 1—Three-quarter Front Right View of Power Plant

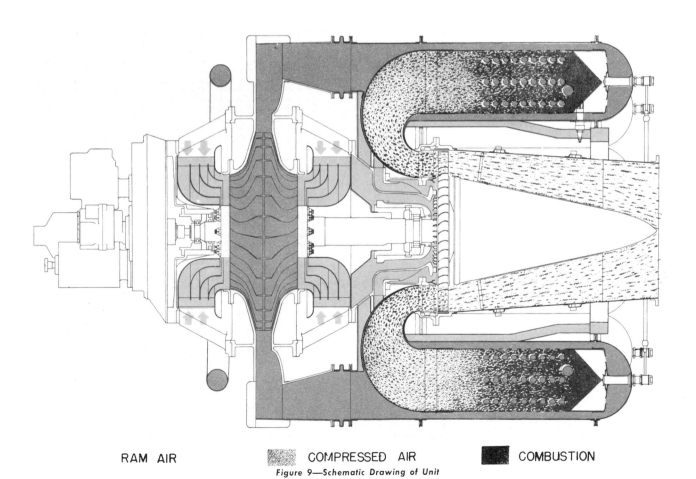

RAM AIR   COMPRESSED AIR   COMBUSTION

Figure 9—Schematic Drawing of Unit

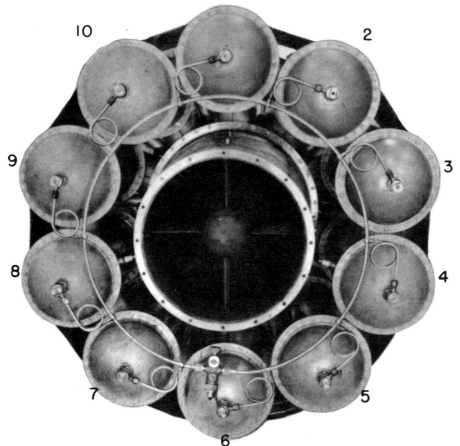

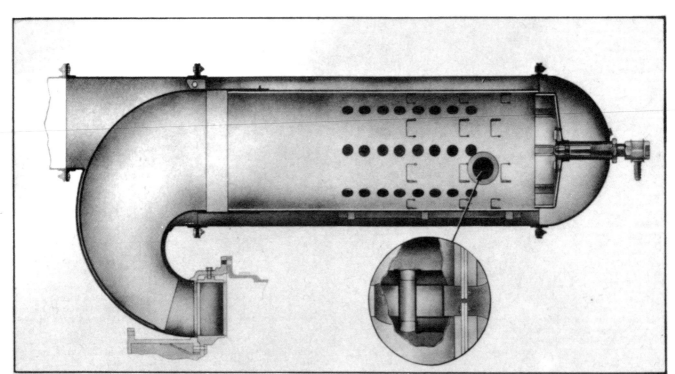

Figure 14—Combustion Chambers

Acknowledgments

A special thanks to Ronald D. Neal of Aerodesign Corp. for the use of his 1966 article in the American Aviation Historical Society Journal.

Other key contributors of text and photos were Jim Wogstadt of Aerophile Publications, R. Eric Falk of GEAE Ohio, as well as Gerry Henderson, Herbert Shaw, Bob Wolf, Ed Merk, Floyd Heglund and Joe Brown of The Jet Pioneers of America.

The Lynn team consisting of Lou Regilio (book cover/design), Nancy Parshley (production/coordination), Dave Parsons (photography), Elisa Hockenhull (graphic layout) and Mary Valentino (typing), deserve additional recognition as does Bob Risch from Lynn Community Relation for his encouragement and support of this project.

To my son Joshua for his insight and original writing, to son Jacob for the time we missed together, and a final acknowledgment to my wife Martha for her understanding of the mess of paraphernalia (during the writing of this book) that has "graced" so much of the fine home she keeps for us.

Thanks and God bless each and all.

Bibliography

General Electric Aircraft Engine Group

    "Seven Decades of Progress"   1979

    "Eight Decades of Progress"   1990

    "We Piloted The First Jet Aircraft

        Coast to Coast" T. Rogers and F. Burnham   1952

    "Service Manual I-16 B4, B5, B7"   1944

    "Service Manual I-A "   1943

    Heiman, Grover "Jet Pioneers,"   1963

    Wolf, Robert "Manuscript,"   1989

    Neal, Ronald D. "The Bell XP-59A Airacomet"

        A.A.H.S. Journal Vol. II-No.3   (Fall 1966)

Honor Roll

Regular Membership

E.L. Auyer
M.O. Bennert
C.F. Benson
J.A. Benson
H.E. Bergdale
A.C. Bertrand
L.C. Blaisdell
W.J. Blaisdell
G.C. Blanchard
A.E. Bobst
H.L. Bowers
P.L. Brodeur
J.E. Brown
C.P. Burkhardt
W.W. Burlan
E. Burr
J.F. Cannon
T. Cave
J.W. Chambers
E.C. Churchill
F.M. Clifford
E.G. Coleman
E.J. Cormier
W.B. Costain
J. Cotton
L.C. Cullen
R.J. Deveney
C.B. Dresser
W.J. Dusty
H.J. Emery
E.R. Fairbanks
C.W. Farrell
Edna V. Farrell
C.R.S. Fernald
M.R. Files
J.E. Foisy
A. Fornoff
G.J. Franklin
G.G. Geromini
W.R. Gibney
W. Gibson
C. Gosden
W.R. Goss
E.S. Groves
F.W. Grunder
W. Gunther
W.R. Hall
G.W. Hay
F.W. Heglund
G.V. Henderson
J.E. Hodan
H.A. Hollis
J. Honour
H.L. Hoyt
J.I. Hull
N. Insana
A.S. Irwin
A.W. Jacobsen
K. Jemison

J. Jewett
H. Joachimi
R.L. Johnson
W.E. Johnson
R.B. Jordan
J. Karolewski
W.H. Kastburg
E.J. Kelley
R.L. Kelley
Ray Keeler
P.H. Knowlton
M. Kowalski
P.R. Kozak
E.O. Kraft
V. Krantz
P. Kushnieruk
W.W. Kuyper
E.A. Lamm
H.H. Langley
G. Laventure
T.R. Lawson
J.R. Leger
E. Leithliter
R.F. Letts
M.R. Locurcio
E.E. MacKay
W.MacRobbie
F. Majeski
S.S. Marcuso
G.H. Manson
E.S. Marek
H. Marek
Jean Maxwell
G.J. McCaul
W. McLaughlin
H.F. Moore
G.F. Moseley
H.H. Munsey
G.S. Nargis
E.C. Newburg
A.W. Nichols
P. Norton
T.A. Pachol
J.M. Park, Jr.
G.T. Payzant
E.C. Peck
G.C. Peddle
J.J. Pescatore
D. Pote
G.W. Price
C. Quillin
E.F. Quinn, Jr.
W.B. Reinhult, Jr.
Col. W.E. Richards
C.P. Roberts
M.G. Robinson
T.J. Rogers
J. Russell
Jerome Ryan

E.S. Sampson
Mary Sargent
F. Sarginson
M.D. Sawdey
J.H. Sedgewick
H.S. Shaw
N. Shelby
F.T. Sheehan
A.G. Silvester
A.R. Smith, Jr.
G.E. Snyder
J. Sorota
J.R. Stanley
Mrs. Horace Stetson III
A.C. Stoffert
R.D. Stoner
Wendall F. Stuart
E.N. Sweeney
W.K. Taylor
R.E. Thompson
E. Uber
B.F. Warren
J. Watkins
J.J. Welland
N. Wessell
F.R. Weymouth
E.L. White
M.G. Wilson
R.A. Wolf

Deceased
Regular Members

W. H. Anderson
C.L. Adrian
G.E. Allen
W.L. Badger
Frank Barraclough
G.R. Berg
T.J. Benson
W. Bethin
L.A.W. Bjorkman
Jules Bosway
F.F. Burnham
J.W. Cann
E.M. Carey
Harry Carr
P.A. Chadwell
E.J. Clark
E.D. Colclough
H. Crane
H.D. Crosby
W.H. Cushman
N.J. Darling
D.L. Desmond
E.N. Downing
R. W. Durland
G.L. Edmondson
T. Elliot

P.C. Emmons
R.F. Finn
J.H. Fleming
S.H. Frankel
Doug Fullerton
F.S. Galusha
F.P. Geary
J. George
C.B. Gleason
W.B. Goddard
W. Gougian
O.G. Green
A. Growitz
E.A. Gustafson
L.M. Hadsall
C. Haigh
R.F. Hall
A.P. Hanson
E.C. Harris
E.O. Hathaway
C. Hendrickson
L. Holden
J.E. Horne, Jr.
G.F. Hubbard
M.E. Jeness
W.J. Johnsyn
R.L. Keene
R.L. Keller
Melvin Kensinger
A. Koldziei
E.B. Leach
L.H. Lechthaler
R.J. Lewis
J.S. Limage
E.T. Lotti
R.V. Lyness
F.J. Lysaght
A.R. Magee
D.M. Marshall
Jack Marshall
C.F. McCool
T.F. McDonald
T.J. McDonald
A.J. McEachern
I.E. Melanson
A.A. Miller
J.C. Miller
J.C. Moore
H.C. Morrison
George Murphy
G.J. Murphy
W.T. Murphy
C.A. Newman
W.I. Nichols
J.A. Nockles
K.G. Ohlson
R.C. Oppen
W.A. Paille
C.P. Pasquina

Jet Pioneers Assoc. Of U.S.A. Distinguished Members

A. Peters
S.E. Plummer
H. Poe
J.B. Powers
W. Powers
H.M. Poyer
Waverly Reeves
R. Rice
G. Richardson
R. Ringle
E.B. Roberts
J. Robertson
R.C. Robin
R. E. Santos
F.E. Shearer
Dr.C.W. Smith
O.E. Snell
K.L. Sowdon
B.O. Sparks
R.M. Springer
E.L. Stevens
A.R. Stevenson, Jr.
H.A. Stott
Dan Stowell
H.E. Stromberg
S. Suchocki
C.T. Sullivan
H.L. Sullivan
H.O. Swain
J. Szalay, Jr.
H.V. Taylor
E.S. Thompson
J.F. Travers
E.M. Tritle
J.G. Trundinger
C.P. Urbon
G.B. Warren
J. Weisbeck, Jr.
E.D. Wharf
P.A. Whitmore
N.M. Wison
A.M. Wirtanen
R.L. Wiseman
Tom Wry
H. Wrzosek
R.H. Yeo
H.A. Zimmer

Joseph Alford
Gen. H.H. Arnold
Jacquel Auriol
L.D. Bell
Maj. Gen. Albert Boyd
Neil Burgess
Ann Baumgartner Carl
W. George Carter
George B.W. Chidlaw
Harry H. Clayton
Jacqueline Cochran
Col. Joseph Cotton
Lt.Gen. L.C. Craigie
Commander James J. Davidson
Dr. Anselm Franz
Peter Girard
Martin Hemsworth
Major Dundas Heenan
Leonard S. Hobbs
Alan Howard
A.M. Tex Johnston
Clarence Johnson
Richard Johnson
Brig. Gen. D.J. Keirn

Major William Knight
Ezra Kotcher
C.W. Lapierre
Fred O. MacFee
Col. John A. Macready
Roy Marquardt
J.S. McDonnell
Col. W.W. Millikan
Dr. S.A. Moss
R.C. Muir
Dr. Osamu Nagano
Capt. J. Slade Nash
Gerhard Neumann
Wright A. Parkins
Frank E. Pickering
Perry Pratt
D.C. Prince
S.R. Puffer
Frederick B. Rentschler
Edgar P. Rhodes
Brian H. Rowe
C.A. Salmonson
Gerry Sayer
Lt. Col. Joseph Schiele
Bernard E. Schmickrath

Major R.W. Schroeder
Commander Alan B. Shepard, Jr.
D.R. Shoults
Arthur S. Smith
R.G. Standerwick
R.M. Stanley
Col. J.F. Stapp
Dale D. Streid
Leo J. Sullivan
Maj.Gen. R.P. Swofford, Jr.
Vice Admiral F.N. Trapnell
Dr. Hans von Ohain
D.F. Warner
Dr. Stewart Way
Andrew V.D. Willgoos
Richard T. Whitcomb
A.S. White
R.P. Whitman
Air Commodore Sir Frank Whittle
C.E. Wilson
Edward Woll
Charles Yeager

Jet Pioneers Assoc. Of U.S.A. Honorary Members

Hiram Anderson, Jr.
Wilber Betts
Donald Button
H.W. Chandler
Malcom J. Dodd
Millard Dowell
Tom J. Dozier
George Durgin
Jack Finlayson
Mrs. Yemba Greene

Charles A. Hall
Col. Grover Heiman
Joseph Higgins
Arthur R. Holbrook
Ray Holl
F.H. Kelley
G.W. Lawson
Richard F. Lederhaus
William Meckley
Nancy Metropolis

Jim Runyon
J.X. Ryneska
W.A. Schoneberger
Archie Simons
Ramond Small
Louis Varadi
Mrs. D.F. Warner
Virgil Weaver
Ralph Wheeler
Edward Woll

Jet Pioneers Assoc. Of U.S.A. Affiliate Members

John Blake
Dave Carpenter
John Kazarosian
Paul S. Larcom

Mike Lemish
Martin M. Lindenauer
John Parkinson
Robert A. Rohrer

Don Thompson
Virginia M. Wilke
B.H. Wood

Dark Print Denotes Deceased Members

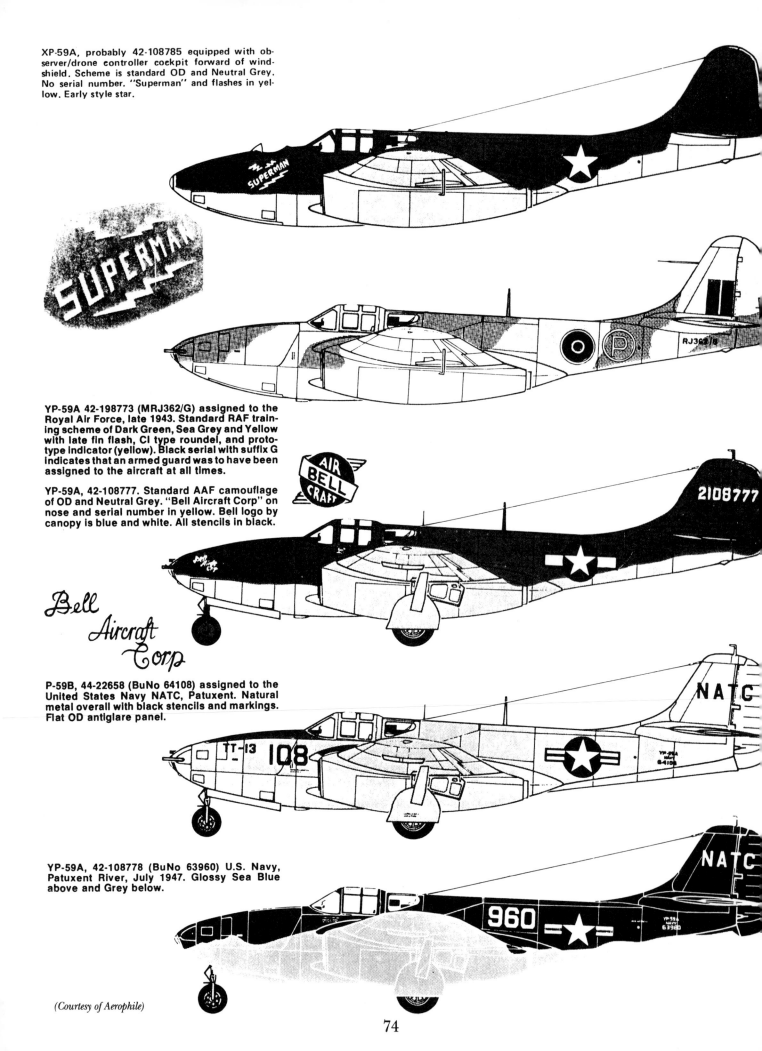

XP-59A, probably 42-108785 equipped with observer/drone controller cockpit forward of windshield. Scheme is standard OD and Neutral Grey. No serial number. "Superman" and flashes in yellow. Early style star.

YP-59A 42-198773 (MRJ362/G) assigned to the Royal Air Force, late 1943. Standard RAF training scheme of Dark Green, Sea Grey and Yellow with late fin flash, CI type roundel, and prototype indicator (yellow). Black serial with suffix G indicates that an armed guard was to have been assigned to the aircraft at all times.

YP-59A, 42-108777. Standard AAF camouflage of OD and Neutral Grey. "Bell Aircraft Corp" on nose and serial number in yellow. Bell logo by canopy is blue and white. All stencils in black.

P-59B, 44-22658 (BuNo 64108) assigned to the United States Navy NATC, Patuxent. Natural metal overall with black stencils and markings. Flat OD antiglare panel.

YP-59A, 42-108778 (BuNo 63960) U.S. Navy, Patuxent River, July 1947. Glossy Sea Blue above and Grey below.

(Courtesy of Aerophile)

74

YP-59A, 42-108783 "Mystic Mistress" drone controller. Standard OD and grey scheme with yellow serial. Black stencils, natural metal drop tank. "Bell" in red and black, "Aircraft" in black on both sides of aircraft. Insignia on left side only.

Badge disc is Sky blue with black border and white clouds. Figure is flesh with yellow hair, gold crown, pin, scepter and dress. Five P-59 aircraft are OD. All outlined black.

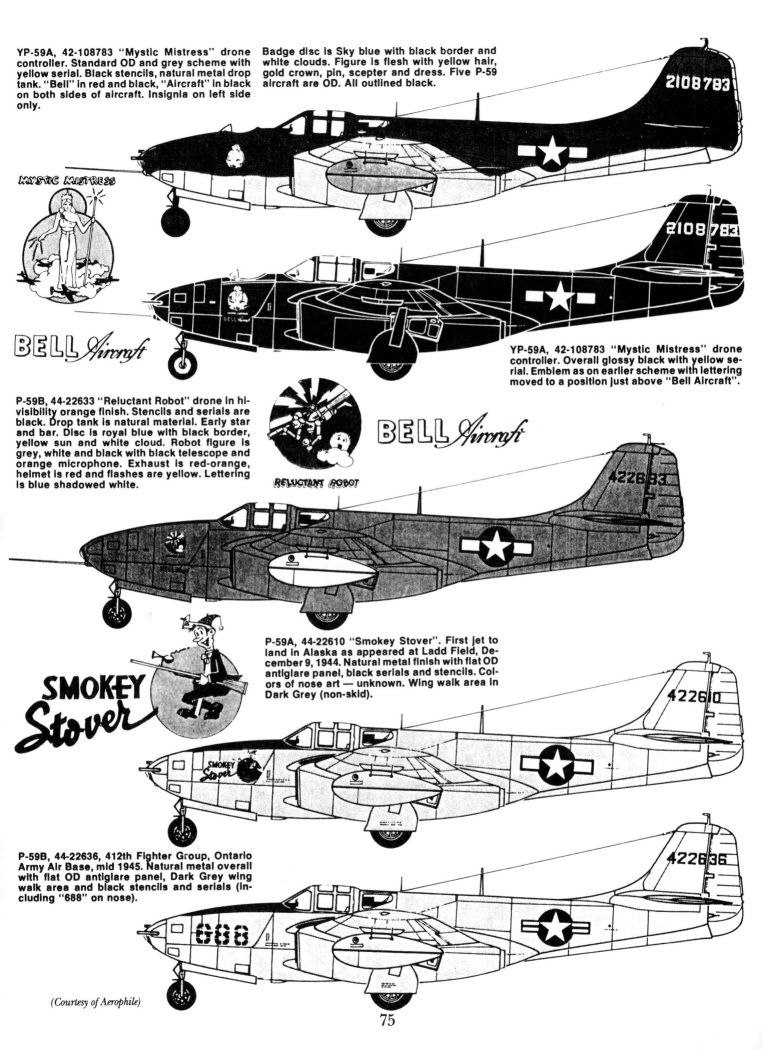

MYSTIC MISTRESS

BELL Aircraft

YP-59A, 42-108783 "Mystic Mistress" drone controller. Overall glossy black with yellow serial. Emblem as on earlier scheme with lettering moved to a position just above "Bell Aircraft".

P-59B, 44-22633 "Reluctant Robot" drone in hi-visibility orange finish. Stencils and serials are black. Drop tank is natural material. Early star and bar. Disc is royal blue with black border, yellow sun and white cloud. Robot figure is grey, white and black with black telescope and orange microphone. Exhaust is red-orange, helmet is red and flashes are yellow. Lettering is blue shadowed white.

BELL Aircraft

RELUCTANT ROBOT

P-59A, 44-22610 "Smokey Stover". First jet to land in Alaska as appeared at Ladd Field, December 9, 1944. Natural metal finish with flat OD antiglare panel, black serials and stencils. Colors of nose art — unknown. Wing walk area in Dark Grey (non-skid).

SMOKEY Stover

P-59B, 44-22636, 412th Fighter Group, Ontario Army Air Base, mid 1945. Natural metal overall with flat OD antiglare panel, Dark Grey wing walk area and black stencils and serials (including "688" on nose).

(Courtesy of Aerophile)

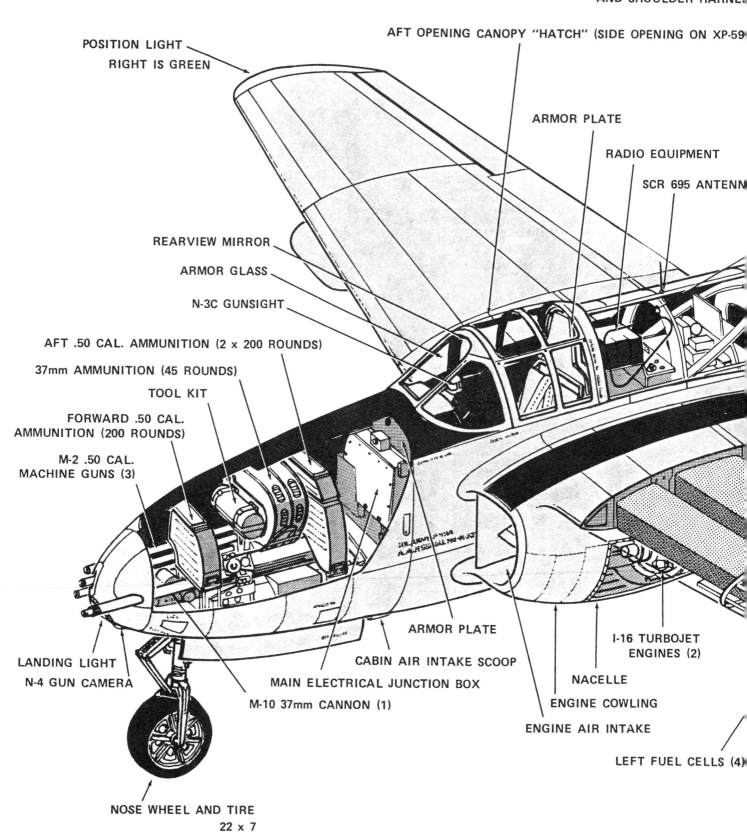

PILOT SEAT WITH LIFE PRESERVER CUSHIO
AND SHOULDER HARNES

AFT OPENING CANOPY "HATCH" (SIDE OPENING ON XP-59

POSITION LIGHT
RIGHT IS GREEN

ARMOR PLATE

RADIO EQUIPMENT

SCR 695 ANTENN

REARVIEW MIRROR

ARMOR GLASS

N-3C GUNSIGHT

AFT .50 CAL. AMMUNITION (2 x 200 ROUNDS)

37mm AMMUNITION (45 ROUNDS)

TOOL KIT

FORWARD .50 CAL.
AMMUNITION (200 ROUNDS)

M-2 .50 CAL.
MACHINE GUNS (3)

ARMOR PLATE

CABIN AIR INTAKE SCOOP

I-16 TURBOJET
ENGINES (2)

MAIN ELECTRICAL JUNCTION BOX

NACELLE

M-10 37mm CANNON (1)

ENGINE COWLING

ENGINE AIR INTAKE

LANDING LIGHT
N-4 GUN CAMERA

LEFT FUEL CELLS (4)

NOSE WHEEL AND TIRE
22 x 7

(Courtesy of Aerophile)

76

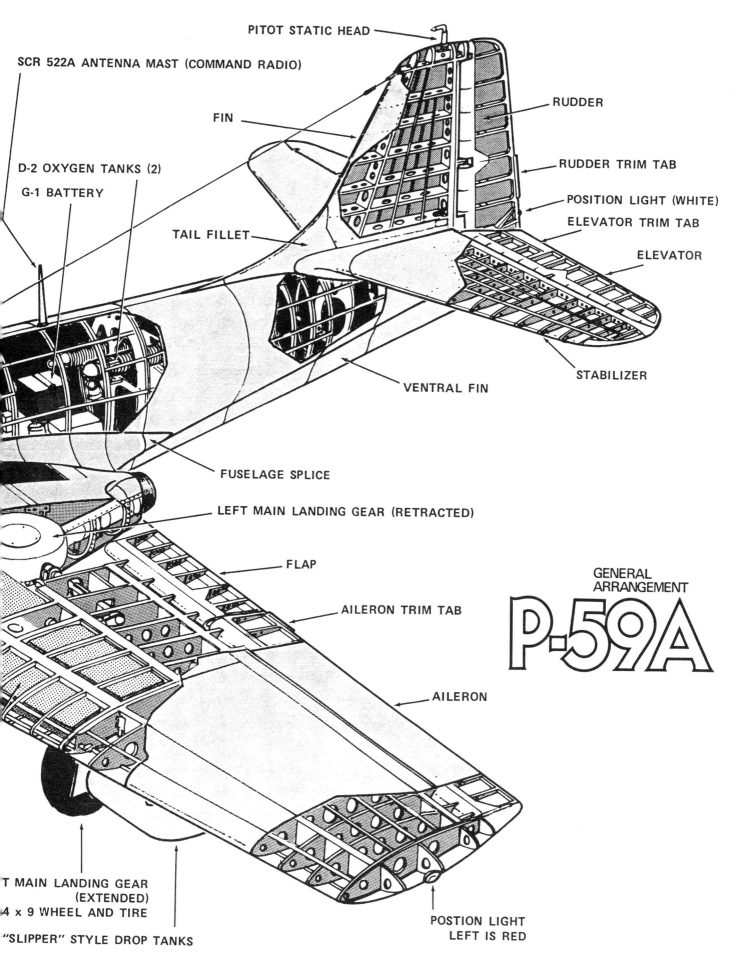

PITOT STATIC HEAD

SCR 522A ANTENNA MAST (COMMAND RADIO)

FIN

D-2 OXYGEN TANKS (2)

G-1 BATTERY

TAIL FILLET

RUDDER

RUDDER TRIM TAB

POSITION LIGHT (WHITE)

ELEVATOR TRIM TAB

ELEVATOR

STABILIZER

VENTRAL FIN

FUSELAGE SPLICE

LEFT MAIN LANDING GEAR (RETRACTED)

FLAP

AILERON TRIM TAB

AILERON

GENERAL
ARRANGEMENT

P-59A

T MAIN LANDING GEAR
(EXTENDED)
4 x 9 WHEEL AND TIRE

"SLIPPER" STYLE DROP TANKS

POSTION LIGHT
LEFT IS RED

David M. Carpenter

A Maine native and graduate of Northeastern University, Dave has worked for General Electric Aircraft Engines since 1963. Presently he is Manager of Spare Parts Sales for the T700 Turboshaft Helicopter engine that powers the Black Hawk and Apache Aircraft.

As a member of the American Helicopter Society, Army Aviation Association of America and The Jet Pioneers of America, Dave has been active in promoting the industry.

This book is the end result of volunteer work starting in 1986 with the JPA. A follow on 6 year effort of collecting documents, filming interviews and editing resulted in this book. Dave makes his home in Danvers, Massachusetts with his wife Martha and sons Joshua and Jacob.

PILOT'S REPORT

Place: **Materiel Center Flight Test Base**   Flight #1

Pilot: Robert M. Stanley

Weather: Wind west, 20 m.p.h., C.A.V.U.

Purpose: Shakedown Flight

Changes Since Last Flight: --

C.G. 26.1 %M.A.C.   Gross Weight 9312 Pounds   Time Take-Off 6PM

1. It was necessary to replace the ignition wire prior to satisfactory start of either engine. The ignition wiring is subjected to more heat than the insulation will stand and it appears inevitable that a redesign of this installation is necessary.

2. The airplane was completely standard as regards configuration for this flight. The aileron trim tabs were set for their maximum servo action. All trim tabs were neutral throughout the flight.

3. Flight testing began with fuel tanks approximately one-half full. The airplane was taxied approximately 3 miles down wind prior to take-off, during which time the interior of the cabin became somewhat stuffy from heat and engine fumes. Upon swinging into the wind for take-off, the engine fumes disappeared.

4. All take-offs were made using 15,000 r.p.m. on both engines with flaps fully up and with the airplane pulled off the ground at about 80 to 90 m.p.h. Throttle was applied promptly and acceleration during take-off appeared quite satisfactory. The run was estimated to be in the vicinity of 2,000 feet, possibly more. The first flight reached an altitude of approximately 25 feet, and landing was made using partial power without flaps. This take-off had the wind approximately 60° on the starboard bow and must be considered a cross-wind take-off.

5. Aileron and elevator action appear satisfactory, although the rudder force appears undesirably light causing the airplane to yaw somewhat for very light pedal pressures. Left rudder was needed for take-off due to cross wind.

6. While taxying back for take-off, the airplane ran at high speed over a small ditch approximately 4" deep without damage to the undercarriage.

7. During taxy and flight, all temperatures remained below their maxima.

Form C1-7

Actual pilot log for October 1, 1942. (Courtesy of JPA)